P9-DTS-463

FORMS OF NATURE AND LIFE

A STUDIO BOOK

ANDREAS FEININGER

FORMS OF NATURE AND LIFE

THE VIKING PRESS · NEW YORK

The specimens shown in plates 57, 122—124, 126—135, 136 (top), 137—138, 139 (bottom), 142—147, 149, 156—159, and 161 are in the collections of the American Museum of Natural History in New York.

Published in 1966 by The Viking Press, Inc.
625 Madison Avenue, New York, N.Y. 10022

Published simultaneously in Canada by
The Macmillan Company of Canada Limited

Library of Congress catalog card number: 66-21802

Printed in the Republic of West Germany by
Kleins Druck-
und Verlagsanstalt GmbH., Lengerich (Westf.)

CONTENTS

INTRODUCTION

As long as I can remember I have been fascinated by the forms of rocks and plants and animals. I have studied these forms not with the eye of the artist but with the eye of the architect and engineer who is primarily interested in structure, construction, and function. I have collected these objects either in their natural state or as photographs and, through the years, have gathered a wealth of material which, I feel, should be as interesting and thought-provoking to many other people as it is to me. Ten years ago I published a collection of my nature photographs in a book, *The Anatomy of Nature,* but I have amassed so much new material that I feel a revised edition of the *Anatomy* is justified.

I am a photographer, not a scientist. But I believe one does not have to be a scientist to be able to appreciate and, within certain limits, to understand the infinitely rich and marvelous aspects of the natural world. In many ways, scientists are like explorers or frontiersmen. They fight at the borders of knowledge to gather the facts necessary to widen our understanding of the physical world. But most if not all of their gains have been and continuously are interpreted by skilled writers on scientific subjects and translated into a language comprehensible to anyone willing to make an effort. There are no mysteries in science as such; the mystery is in the phenomena which science investigates. Many things will always remain inexplicable, such as the concepts of infinity and the beginning of time. Although scientists are able to measure with superb accuracy the frequencies of the electromagnetic radiation which we perceive as color, they are unable to explain how the sensation of color occurs within the brain. Nor can they explain the psychological effects of color, or the enjoyment which we derive from color harmonies, from music, or from works of art. We understand intellectually, but we enjoy emotionally. Few people understand, as far as understanding is possible, the physics of color, but most are moved by the beauty of a flaming sunset. Few people are sufficiently trained to appreciate the structural beauty of a symphony, but that does not prevent them from enjoying music. It is in this sense, through feeling and empathy, that I attempt to show the reader some of the wonders among which he lives.

The main subject of this book is not beauty but the interrelationship of structure, function, and form. Many picture books have been compiled to persuade people that nature is beautiful. But the kind of beauty stressed in those books is, in my opinion, superficial—beauty experienced merely as ornament without relation to purpose and evaluated in anthropomorphic terms. Nature is never beautiful solely in this sense. If objects in nature are beautiful, they are so for a reason. In the main, nature is practical, even more so than man. Its forms are functional shapes evolved from necessity. And precisely because they are functional, we feel these forms are beautiful.

We are only now beginning to appreciate this kind of beauty in the works of man. Perhaps this new awareness is an outgrowth of our changing social structure. As our cost of living rises, it becomes less and less desirable to add to the rising cost of production by embellishing things with ornaments which do nothing to increase their usefulness. Perhaps it is simply a sign of maturity in matters of taste, an inner honesty which no longer needs the crutch of disguise. This new beauty—form freed from superfluous additions whose purpose was to conceal and pretend—is already apparent in the pillars and curves of our suspension bridges and the glass curtain-walls of skyscrapers. We find it in the shapes of modern furniture and tableware, in typewriter and office-furniture design, and in microscopes and all other scientific precision instruments. It is from this point of view that I have approached the functional forms of nature.

As I examined them, lived with them, speculated about them, I found that completely unrelated structures often show a surprising similarity, indicating the presence of basic principles in nature. Layers of water-deposited sedimentary rock and the annual growth rings of wood, for example, if photographically presented in the same scale, appear virtually identical, indicating that the records of time are manifested in the same way in wood and stone. Formed layer by layer in a process of accretion—each layer added by a season's growth, a year, a period of dryness, flood, or inundation—these structures accurately document the passage of time in terms of growing seasons, flood or drought, or periods when the land stood above water or was submerged beneath it. The stiffening veins of many leaves and those of certain insect wings prove by their similarity of arrangement that the structural problems underlying both are identical: a membrane must be stiffened to become self-supporting. The venom of wasps and the poisons from stinging jellyfish and nettles—secretions of an insect, a coelenterate, and a plant—are primarily a mixture of the same three hormones: acetylcholine, serotonine, and histamine. And protective spines are more or less alike whether they occur in a plant, a mammal, an insect, or a shell. Perhaps this is so because everything in nature is constructed from the same basic materials. And atoms combine to form molecules, and molecules to form matter, in only a limited number of ways. But at what point do they come to life? Where can we draw the line between living things and inanimate objects? Does such a dividing line even exist? Dead crystals grow as if they were alive, and live viruses, when desiccated, crumble and crystallize like minerals, only to come back to life again when conditions are right. Actually all the elements of which living organisms consist are nothing but inanimate matter—atoms, elements, chemical compounds—and yet, combined in certain ways, they constitute life.

It is the purpose of this book to document the unity of natural things, their similarity, and their interdependence; to show the beauty of the living functional form; and to make you recognize your relationship to the rocks and the plants and the animals—you, a human being, an integral part of nature, a part of the universe.

To experience the unity of all life, take an early morning walk in the woods when, with the force of an explosion, generated some eight minutes earlier ninety-three million miles away in the thermonuclear furnace of the sun, the light of a new day, in slanting shafts of mist, bursts upon the earth. A new morning, an new day, a measure of change and evolution—birth, growth, maturity, decline, death, and decay—and out of decaying matter new life rising again.

Attune yourself to your environment until you feel part of it. You will find wonders in the immense diversity of life, the intricacy of its manifestations. Wherever you look there is life. Dormant seeds, some as small as grains of sand, bear within their shells the future flowering plant. Pine cones massing on the forest floor have already spent their wealth of seeds which in time will grow to towering trees. Marvel that each seed, no larger than a grain of rice, contains the pattern for a giant tree, complete with all its diversifications of wood and bark and flowers and leaves; trunk, branches, root, and crown; latent, yet ready to burst forth with elemental force when its time has arrived, in growth rooting to the dark earth, reaching lightward to reproduce its kind.

Compare the seeds from various plants. Often, they look more or less alike; some are even indistinguishable from one another. And yet, invariably, inevitably, each of these will develop into a certain kind of plant and no other. Nowhere in nature, it seems to me, can the mysteries of life and growth be felt more strongly than in the contemplation of a seed.

Study the inventiveness which nature uses to ensure the spread of plants, the multitude of ingenious devices for the dispersal of seeds. Some hook to the coats of animals and fall away as the creature roves. Others are scattered by birds that feed upon the fruit but eliminate the indigestible seeds. Still others fall to closer grounds, shot to distances of several yards when the drying fruit pods split open with a snap. Some travel with ocean currents and tides, remaining buoyant for months, retaining power to germinate and grow on distant island soils. But the greatest number travel with the wind, gliding on gossamer parachutes like the dandelion seeds; spinning in spiral flight and fall, on miniature propeller form, like the maple seeds; or whirling in rolling race with prairie winds to shake from the parent husk, like the seeds of the tumbleweed.

Notice the animals and plants around you. A squirrel watches you from its perch, curious, distrustful, half hidden behind the bole of a tree. A spider waits motionless in its web. Armies of caterpillars chew away at leaves. Worms tunnel the ground, converting leaf mold to humus. Fungi and bacteria break down decaying matter into organic compounds which in time will nourish new life. The air itself vibrates with sound and motion, the wing beats of insects, the song and call of birds, the ceaseless whispering of boughs and leaves rustled by the gentle morning winds.

You become aware of the interdependence of all life, animals and plants, all of nature's creations. And you realize with sharp clarity that you too are part of this immensity of nature, a humble yet important part, earth-bound, mortal, dependent for survival upon animal and plant, and that the atoms in your body are identical with those that make up the rocks, the plants, the animals, the earth, moon, sun, and stars.

In a corner of my window, which overlooks a wide Connecticut valley, a spider has made its home. Ever since it was so small that I could hardly see it—a semitransparent, animated speck scuttling along on eight minuscule legs, thin as the finest hair—I have watched this spider go about its way of life. Motionless for hours and days, it patiently waits for tiny flies to become enmeshed in its web. This spider does not hunt for food. It depends upon chance captures for survival. It depends upon others; it cannot survive alone.

Except for the autophytes—bacteria living on iron or sulphur—no animal and few plants can exist independently of others. Each plays a part in the great symphony of life. Spiders are one of nature's regulating devices which prevent insects from increasing in such numbers that they would destroy all plant life and themselves die of starvation. But without insects, many flowers and trees would become extinct; being totally dependent upon pollination by insects, they could no longer reproduce their kind. Without such plants, many animals could not exist. Without green plants, there would be neither animals nor man because both depend upon green plant life for their existence. This is so because one of the necessities of life is carbon. Every molecule of every bit of living tissue is built around an atom of carbon. And although carbon is a constituent of the atmosphere, animals cannot absorb it from the air by respiration, but can obtain it only by eating plants.

This is the carbon cycle: carbon is united with oxygen to form carbon dioxide, one of the gases of the atmosphere. Through minute openings in their leaves, green plants absorb this gas. Within the leaf, the gas is combined with water (absorbed by the roots and transported through the stem to the leaf) to form sugar. This process of photosynthesis is powered by light and engineered by chlorophyll. Plant-eating animals obtain the carbon without which they cannot build their tissues by eating green plants. Flesh-eating animals obtain carbon by eating animals that have fed on plants.

Carbon is one of the earth's less abundant elements; carbon dioxide constitutes only 0.03 per cent of the air's volume. Animals exhale carbon, and green plants, too, return carbon dioxide to the atmosphere through respiration. In addition, some carbon is continually liberated through combustion of organic matter in fires and furnaces all over the world and through volcanic seepage from the molten interior of the earth. However, all the carbon in the atmosphere would have been exhausted long ago—fixed within organic living matter or buried in the ground, as a large part is now buried in the form of coal, limestone, and oil, or dissolved in the sea—were it not for fungi and bacteria. Their role in the great cyclic drama of life is to break down dead organic matter into its basic compounds. And in doing this they free carbon to enter once more the cycle needed for all life. And so it is that the carbon in your body cells may have once been part of a tree, an animal, or a man—living perhaps thousands of years ago. And in time this same carbon will help sustain other forms of life.

The gaseous exchange in green plants consists of two parts: photosynthesis and respiration. In the first process, carbon dioxide is used and oxygen released as a by-product; in the second, oxygen is used while carbon dioxide is released. However, these two exchanges do not cancel out because photosynthesis proceeds at a higher rate than respiration. The result is that, on the whole, plants liberate more oxygen than they consume and use more carbon dioxide than they return to the air. This is another vitally important factor in the perpetuation of life because, otherwise, already within a few hundred years, the supply of free oxygen would be exhausted—fixed in the form of solid chemical compounds—while enough carbon dioxide would have accumulated within the atmosphere to poison all animal life, including the life of man.

A third element vital to the existence of life is nitrogen, which is also an essential component of protoplasm, that mysterious substance which is life. Nearly four-fifths of the atmosphere consists of nitrogen, but, as with carbon, animals can absorb it only by eating plants, or indirectly by eating other animals. But green plants cannot absorb nitrogen as they can absorb carbon from the air.

Again, it is left to certain kinds of bacteria to complete the cyclic fabric of life. Living symbiotically in the roots of many plants, particularly legumes, from which they obtain their carbon, these nitrogen-fixing bacteria have a unique power. They are able to absorb the life-giving nitrogen directly from the air and convert it into proteins. These proteins are absorbed by the roots of the plants from the protoplasm from which the bacteria obtained their food. Dead and decaying, decomposed by saprophytes—plants, fungi, and microbes living on dead organic matter—and broken down into basic compounds by molds and ammonifying bacteria, these plants in time surrender their borrowed nitrogen to the soil to be drawn upon by new plants according to their needs. Or the plants provide the animals or humans who eat them with essential nitrogen which, after death, is returned to the soil to be recycled again.

As I look at the web of my little spider it seems to me a structure worthy of as much admiration as any structure created by man. It is an incarnation of pure geometry, spun from silk the tensile strength of which surpasses that of structural steel. Like any creation of nature, it is functional, designed for a definite purpose, constructed with marvelous economy to achieve maximum efficiency with a minimum expenditure of material. It has clarity and symmetry of organization. And it derives from these basic qualities a particular kind of beauty which far surpasses that of man's ornamental designs. A spider web has the elemental beauty which we find in the symbols of Euclidian geometry, in parabolic curves and in snow crystals. We also find it in flower shapes which nature designed not as objects of beauty but as devices for propagation. We recognize it in the shapes of bones which, rivaling in abstract beauty the sculpture of Brancusi and Arp, are formed to bear the strains and stresses to which they are exposed. We see such beauty in nature wherever we look and, although we often may not comprehend what underlies it, the more closely we look the more we find to enjoy. No one has given better expression to this than Dr. Roman Vishniac, superb photographer of everything minute in nature, who once said: "Everything made by human hands looks terrible under magnification—crude, rough, and unsymmetrical. But in nature every bit of life is lovely. And the more magnification we use, the more details are brought out, perfectly formed, like endless sets of boxes within boxes."

To enter this magic world of the minute, carry on your walks a pocket magnifier and look closely at whatever you encounter. Wherever you look you will make discoveries. Here is a moth hugging the bark of a tree, passing the day in sleep, its protective design rendering it all but invisible. Study this design through your lens and marvel at its symmetry—each tiny dot and curlicue on one side has its counterpart on the other. How did the moth come to grow that way? Where is that stupenduous plan that dictates the position of every molecule in its wings?

Look at the eyes of a horsefly, that biting pest that you just swatted, and find a pair of faceted jewels which, in the glory of their iridescent reds and greens, rival rubies and emeralds. Do not overlook that little turquoise capsule hanging from a twig, its rim encrusted with silver. It is the chrysalis of the monarch butterfly, one of our largest and most beautiful day-flying insects. Give it a minute's thought. See with your mind's eye the caterpillar, that sluggish sausage stuffed with vegetable matter whose only purpose in life seems to be to eat. See it approach the end of its journey, probing around restlessly, instinctively searching for the spot where that Cinderella performance will take place, that magic act that transforms the crawling slug into a lofty creature of the air. Imagine what this involves, and what happens: having tied itself securely by its hindmost pair of legs with silken bonds to a twig, the caterpillar hangs straight down and, motionless, awaits the great event. Gradually, it seems to shrink, it shrivels, it splits, the skin peels off, and out of its discarded hide the shiny chrysalis emerges, that jeweled vessel within the walls of which the caterpillar dissolved. Yes, it literally dissolved, it liquefied itself, and if you were to open the chrysalis all you would find inside would be a viscous fluid. Eventually, the glittering butterfly will break its turquoise prison, ascend to the end of the twig, expand its wings, and fly away into the light. How did this magic happen? How is it possible that a living caterpillar liquefies its body, completely remakes itself, and turns itself into a butterfly—a creature so totally unlike its former self that one who did not know the story would never suspect the truth?

Take a close look at a hover fly, that golden beelike insect which, in miniature helicopter fashion, can stand still in the air, inspect a flower, and dart away forward, sideways, or backward. If you move slowly and carefully you might even induce it to alight on your fingertip and bring it close for inspection. You will find it a thought-provoking creature. Its head, unusually large in proportion to the rest of its body, is almost completely covered by two enormous compound eyes that have a metallic shine like faceted copper orbs. In between are three minute black specks, simple eyes, which are thought to reinforce the light impressions gathered by the compound eyes. Two small, bristle-like structures are antennae, in which insects carry organs sensitive to touch and smell. Beneath, the tongue-like proboscis is in almost constant motion, probing, tasting, eagerly lapping up traces of salt from your fingertip. The finely veined, crystal-clear wings rest horizontally, poised for instant take-off, folded to form a triangle in the latest swept-back, jet-wing fashion. Only when the insect is completely at rest does it fold its wings parallel to its body. This body consists of two clearly defined parts, the thorax which supports the wings and legs, and the abdomen which in the hover fly is boldly striped in black and yellow—warning colors used by both nature and man. But the hover fly is completely harmless, a defenseless creature that neither bites nor stings. Other insects exist which have made these colors respected by rightfully carrying the black-and-yellow flag: the bees and wasps which, as any creature from man to bird and toad knows either instinctively or from painful experience, are perfectly capable of successfully defending their lives. Is it too much to assume that the hover fly, through eons of evolutionary change, has gradually usurped these warning colors in an effort to gain the respect which bees and wasps enjoy, fooling the uninitiated into assuming it is a member of their stinging tribe?

As you watch the hover fly inspect your hand you will see it pause from time to time to clean its already immaculate little person: it lays its front legs to its proboscis and strokes downward, then places its hind legs on top of its already shining wings and brushes rearwards as if to remove invisible specks of dust. And after you have watched it for a while you will become fond of your hover fly and see it with new eyes—see the marvelously organized speck of animated matter that senses and acts and has a brain, be it ever so primitive and small; this miraculous piece of machinery that sees and feels and smells, that anticipated the helicopter and found a way to make life safer for itself by imitating its armed peers; this little golden fly that carries within its tiny body the means to reproduce its kind, to persevere and stay alive in the face of tremendous odds, basking in the sun's warmth, responding joyously to the eternal call of heat and light.

You will develop a new respect for all nature's creations, and will never again willfully and without good reason kill another animal or destroy another plant.

My little spider has grown into a fair-sized spider and by now its web is as large as my hand. And seeing this exquisite structure each morning I cannot help speculating how a spider acquires its spinning skill. No parent taught it—most spiders disperse as soon as they leave the egg, each striking out on its own. The act of spinning is instinctive—an inheritance handed down through generations of spiders since time immemorial. But by what physical means is this ability transferred—not only the compulsion to spin, but also the pattern according to which the web is fashioned, for each species has a different web? The secret must lie in the arrangement of the molecules within a certain gene. But how can a sequence of molecules—a string of matter—pass on anything as insubstantial as knowledge, a drive, a skill, a design, on and on, indefinitely?

If you are a lover of mystery, you will be fascinated by the biological sciences, for they offer limitless food for thought and opportunities for exploration. And although much has been written about the fabulous performances of certain animals, little or nothing beyond the actual facts is known. Here are some of the phenomena that testify to our ignorance:

Green turtles are marine animals that live on seaweed off the coast of South America; but they do not lay their eggs on its shore. On the other hand, it is known that green turtles breed on Ascension Island, which is a forsaken speck of rock right in the middle of the South Atlantic Ocean. In an effort to find out whether these are the same turtles, scientists tagged a number of specimens and discovered that these animals actually are born on Ascension Island, migrate to the coast of Brazil, live there for a few years, then swim back across more than a thousand miles of trackless ocean waste to return to their native island, where they mate and lay their eggs. What unknown instinct drives these turtles back to the place of their birth? What is that nameless sense that enables them to find their way across a thousand miles of water to make landfall unerringly on that minuscule pile of rock?

And the same questions can be asked of the king salmon, which, in search of food, ranges as far west as the central Aleutian Islands only to return, when the time is right, across some twenty-five hundred miles of ocean to its native spawning grounds in the Columbia and Snake Rivers. The European and American fresh-water eels migrate from their native rivers to the Sargasso Sea in the South Atlantic Ocean, there to spawn and die. But their larvae—the elvers, the Leptocephali—make the same migration in reverse, a journey of several thousand miles that may take from one-half to two years to complete, following the ocean currents until they arrive at their ancestral rivers in Europe or America. There they mature and live until they too perceive the call and a nameless instinct drives them to abandon the comfort of their feeding grounds, set out to sea, and depart on that last voyage from which they will not return.

Well-publicized and spectacular are the migratory feats of birds. An arctic tern, ringed as a nestling on the coast of Labrador, was retaken ninety days later and nine thousand miles away in Africa. Another tern, banded in arctic Russia, was picked up off the Australian coast after having flown more than fourteen thousand miles. The sandpiper migrates from Canada to the southern part of South America and often does not stop until it reaches the southernmost tip of Tierra del Fuego. The European stork and European and American swallows regularly make migratory journeys twice a year that involve distances from seven thousand to nine tousand miles.

But spectacular as the distances which birds can travel may be, still more spectacular are their navigational feats. Golden plovers, taking off from Alaska, find their winter homes in the Hawaiian Islands across some two thousand miles of open water. The bristle-thighed curlew, a shore bird summering in Alaska, spends the winter in Tahiti and nearby Pacific islands after having crossed some six thousand miles of water. A Manx shearwater, taken from its home on Skokholm Island, off the coast of Wales, to Boston and released there, was back at its nest twelve days later after a flight of three thousand miles. What is that unknown force that tells these travelers—these tiny packages of energy driven by an indomitable spirit through night and storm toward some distant goal—when to leave, where to go, and how to get there? We do not know. Scientists have many theories, a large number of facts, and as yet no convincing explanation.

The members of the solitary wasp tribe build individual nests for their progeny. When the nest is finished, it must be stocked with food for the grub. But unlike the grubs of the bee, the larvae of the solitary wasps need fresh meat; how can this meat be kept from spoiling in the summer heat? The solitary wasp found a solution: having hunted down its prey—most often a caterpillar, an insect, or a spider of the specific kind which that species of wasp requires—it stings its victim with never-failing anatomical skill in that precise spot where its poison will paralyze the prey but not kill it. Having accomplished this fantastic feat of surgery, which it performs instinctively the way uncounted generations of wasps did before it, it transports its victim to its prepared nest, deposits it in the cell, lays a single egg on it, and seals the entrance. When the larva hatches, it finds itself on a stockpile of food that will keep fresh until the grub is ready to begin its metamorphosis, from which it will emerge as a fully fledged wasp, complete with the awareness of how to care for its issue. How did this instinct develop—this anatomical knowledge that tells the wasp how to paralyze but not to kill? By trial and error? The chances of success must have been almost incalculably small, and failure meant extinction. But how else?

A common sight along wintery New England roads are the nests of the oriole—small gray pouches hanging from the ends of slender branches above the highway. These woven nests are suspended with almost unbelievable skill from the supporting twigs and can withstand forces of over thirty pounds thrust against their sides before they tear away—hurricane forces which would break the branch and uproot the tree long before they ripped the nest from its moorings. Nobody taught the parent bird how to construct such nests—their skill is instinctive. But how did it begin? Why did these birds abandon the traditional easy way of building nests on a foundation of solid branches in the crotch of a tree, and suspend them instead precariously, but so much safer from predators, from the outermost tips of twigs?

One of the most amazing methods of self-defense in the entire animal world is used by the bombardier beetle. This insect carries at the end of its abdomen a swiveling nozzle which it can aim accurately at an aggressor threatening it from any direction—front, sides, or rear. When attacked, the beetle instantly aims its weapon and with uncanny accuracy discharges a poisonous spray which produces convulsions in ants and effectively discourages even such formidable predators as spiders, praying mantises, and toads. What makes this method of defense unique is the fact that the deterrent is not simply a poisonous fluid squirted out under pressure, but the result of a complex chemical reaction which literally produces an internal explosion within the body of the beetle itself. Three chemicals—a hydrogen peroxide and two hydroquinone compounds—are secreted by glands and stored in a reservoir. When triggered in self-defense, a valve opens and the secretions flow into a second hard-walled compartment—a kind of reaction-chamber—where they combine with an enzyme which, acting as a catalyst, produces a chemical reaction of such violence that it can only be called an explosion. And it is this explosion that propels the deterrent.

Stenodus is the name of an aquatic beetle whose traditional enemy is the waterstrider, a long-legged, spider-like bug able to walk on water. When *stenodus* finds itself attacked by a waterstrider, it turns and flees, leaving a few drops of a detergent-like wetting agent in its wake. This wetting agent, which *stenodus* produces in special abdominal glands, destroys the thin elastic boundary-layer between water and air on which the waterstrider walks, causing the pursuer to sink and drown.

Independently of one another, many kinds of animals—particularly salt-water fishes, jellyfishes, squids, crustaceans, and insects, but also some fungi and bacteria—have solved the problem of producing heatless light (bioluminescence). The chemistry of this highly complex process is still not fully understood, although it is known that it is based upon the combination of an enzyme—luciferase—with a fat—luciferin—in an oxidation process which produces light that gives off only 1/80,000 the amount of the heat of a candle flame producing the same degree of illumination. Some of the owners of this light use it to attract prey and to communicate with one another in the silent language of flickering light. In others, it seems to be only a useless quirk of evolution.

Bats are able to fly in total darkness without ever bumping into objects because they use a sonar-like navigational aid based upon echo-location. In flight, they emit high-frequency cries which are inaudible to the human ear but can be detected by instruments. These ultrasonic sound waves are reflected by obstacles in the flight path of the bat, their echo informing the bat of the presence and location of obstacles. This much is known. But how the bat distinguishes between obstacles to be avoided and insects to be caught is still a mystery.

The pit vipers—copperheads, cottonmouths, rattlesnakes—have unique sensing devices between their eyes and nostrils which are sensitive to infrared radiation (heat). These organs, which are directional, enable the snake to pick up the infrared body waves given off by all warm-blooded animals and thus help it to locate and strike at its prey.

The squids possess a unique and "ultra-modern" mode of locomotion: they swim by jet-propulsion. Water entering the "mantle"—the muscular outer envelope of the squid—is compressed by muscular action and forcibly expelled through the "funnel," a conical tube which the squid can at will point backward or forward. It is the push of this jet of water which propels the squid forward or backward easily and fast.

Fascinating and mysterious are the phenomena of life, endlessly varied, infinitely rewarding to the contemplative mind. But one does not have to search far afield or look for the unusual, the bizarre, or the unique to find stimulating food for thought. Some of the most fascinating events occur right within our own body. There is the breakdown and assimilation of food, a physico-chemical process of incredible complexity; the role that hormones, enzymes, and vitamins play as growth regulators and supervisors of every function of the body; procreation and heredity involving reactions of such unimaginable delicacy that the presence or absence of single molecules can make the difference between genius and idiocy, life and death.

What are the causes of immunity? Why are we safe from some diseases but not from others? Why are some people allergic to certain irritants which have no harmful effects on others? What is pain? What triggers the processes of healing and regeneration? How does the brain work? What is consciousness? Or memory? Or thought?

In the presence of such mysteries, it is difficult to understand why most people have so little reverence for life. They kill needlessly without giving a thought to the marvels they destroy. It is almost as if a compulsion were at work, an atavistic instinct reaching out through the dark tunnel of time from the days of the carnivorous apes which, as first shown by Dr. Raymond A. Dart in his book. *Adventures with the Missing Link,* were the progenitors of man.

The urge to destroy is already evident in the child who, encouraged by its thoughtless mother, picks pretty flowers only to cast them aside again before reaching home. It comes out in the hunting instinct of boys who, armed first with a BB gun and later with a .22, go out to shoot small birds and animals "for fun." It is manifest in the housewife who indiscriminately squashes every "bug" unfortunate enough to have blundered into her home. We can observe it in those who clear a building site of every tree because it is cheaper to work on an empty stretch of ground, although the eventual losses in beauty and comfort by far exceed the small initial gain. But the personification of the killer instinct is the hunter to whom killing animals is a "sport"; where the purpose of the hunt is not to provide meat to feed a family but to collect a "trophy"—another bird or fish to "stuff," another head to hang on the wall to proclaim the prowess of the hunter; another animal needlessly killed in its prime, deprived of its right to live in freedom under the sun, its right to procreate and pass on its strength and beauty to future generations—always the biggest, the strongest, the most beautiful, because man's vanity demands a "record" to titillate his ego.

I remember an incident that occurred on a duck hunt which I covered as a photographer for *Life*. A group of hunters deployed along a narrow strip of land connecting two lakes. Flights of ducks passed overhead, each flight greeted with a barrage of lead. And then a solitary pair of ducks came winging and whistling side by side like two arrows, straight and fast. But not quite fast enough. One of the two was hit and quickly lost height, slanted downward, splashed into the water. The other bird continued its flight, apparently unharmed. But he did not go far. He circled back and returned to look for his fallen mate, swooping low over her pitifully flapping form. Twice gunfire drove him away; three times he returned, the third time to fall, riddled with shot, dead beside his companion.

The record of Western man's attitude toward nature is not a pretty one. Motivated more often by greed than need, through overgrazing and overcultivation he has turned pasture land into desert on a world-wide scale; destroyed watersheds through deforestation, and loosed devastating floods which often in a single flash ripped away fertile soil that took thousands of years to build up; polluted rivers and poisoned the very air he breathes; exterminated whole species of animals. According to the latest information, only some seven hundred trumpeter swans are left in the United States, sixty condors, thirty-two wild whooping cranes. On the other hand, the population of the United States is rapidly climbing toward the two-hundred-million mark, and most economists, civic leaders, and businessmen rejoice at this sign of what they call "healthy growth." Growth is a marvelous thing—in the right place. But there must come a time for growth to stop if it is not to degenerate into monstrosity and horror. And this moment is rapidly approaching in regard to human population growth. If the present "population explosion" is permitted to continue unchecked, the number of people will soon reach staggering proportions.

The British physicist John H. Fremlin, in an article which appeared in *Time*, November 13, 1964, says that at its present rate of growth the world's population, which today is around three billion, will double every thirty-seven years. Simple arithmetic tells us that it will take only ten times thirty-seven, or three hundred and seventy years, until the number of people has increased a thousandfold. This means that for every person living today there will be a thousand men, women, and children living in the year 2335, or a total of some three thousand billion people. By artificially melting the polar icecaps with nuclear energy and intensely farming the reclaimed regions, the world's population can be quintupled again and brought up to fifteen thousand billion people. If all the world's animals are destroyed and eliminated as competitors for food, and if food is synthetized out of energy, mineral matter, and waste products including homogenized human cadavers, the earth will be able to sustain one million billion people, raising the population density to two people per every ten square feet of ground. The end, according to Fremlin, will come in less than a thousand years. By that time, there will be some sixty million billion people who will live, twelve people on every square foot of ground, in gigantic air-conditioned structures two thousand stories high. But the enormous amounts of heat produced by this astronomic number of people and their machinery will heat the very surface of the earth to a glowing cherry red.

This is not a nightmare out of science fiction but a pragmatic scientist's sober projection of present trends into the future. To my mind, it is a prospect more terrifying than the specter of thermonuclear war. Yet it will come to pass as inevitably as the sun will rise tomorrow unless concerted efforts to prevent it are made on an international scale immediately.

No thoughtful person can fail to speculate about the causes of Western man's selfishness, shortsightedness, and destructiveness. And it seems to me that the underlying motivation—and justification—has its roots in his religious beliefs. Flattering himself that he is created in the image of God, he sees himself endowed with godlike powers, gifted with godlike wisdom, the master of his environment, of everything that is and lives—his to use, his to exploit, and his, if he wishes, to destroy. And so he goes on raping the land, killing its animals, cutting down its trees, dumping his waste into the rivers, and polluting the air until he destroys his life-giving environment and in his abysmal ignorance, vanity, and greed endangers his very existence.

How different from this is the attitude of the peoples of the Far East toward nature. One of the tenets of Hindu ethics, for example, is profound compassion toward all life. Seeing God in everything, the Hindu feels reverence for everything—elephant or ant, small weed or giant tree. Likewise, the Five Precepts of the Buddhist—a practical code of conduct—forbid the taking of life. And one of the main principles of Chinese religious thought, and an indispensable necessity for the attainment of spiritual satisfaction and peace of mind, is to achieve harmony between man and nature. Whereas Western man sees himself as the crowning glory of creation, the devout Chinese considers himself merely another part of nature, important but not privileged. And while Western man believes himself to have the right to subjugate nature for his own materialistic ends, the Chinese regards nature as an aesthetic pageant whose sublime order and beauty are there to be enjoyed and treasured.

Fortunately—because the future of mankind depends on this—the trends which lead toward eventual destruction of our environment are slowly being reversed, not as a result of basic changes in our philosophy, but because we are finally realizing that ruthless exploitation of natural resources is unprofitable. Despite the pressure of certain vested interests which, shortsightedly and out only for quick and easy gain, are trying desperately to stem this tide, the tide of conservation is rising. Protective laws are being passed which make it illegal to kill certain animals which are on the brink of extinction. Hunting others is regulated in accordance with the available supply. Wilderness areas are set aside so that future generations will have a chance to see the land as it was, wild and beautiful. Federal land is no longer as wide open for exploitation by private grazing and mining interests. More and more towns are adopting zoning laws to ensure orderly expansion instand of putting up with cancerous growth. Factories, furnaces, and incinerators are being regulated and policed to reduce atmospheric pollution to a minimum, and new automobiles must be equipped with devices that prevent excessive discharge of fumes. Sewage treating plants are being built in an effort to clean up streams, rivers, and lakes. Forward-looking timber companies plant more trees than they cut down for lumber and pulp, safeguarding our watersheds and at the same time insuring a continuous harvest of wood—and profits. Lakes and streams are being restocked with fish. And in Africa, a steadily increasing number of safaris leave for the bush with hunters who carry cameras instead of guns, their trophies color slides instead of heads.

I believe that each of us must do his share if he wants his children to live in a better world than the one into which he himself was born. This means working toward family planning and birth control, voting for conservation and zoning laws, teaching our youth to keep the outdoors as clean as their homes, and placing refuse where it belongs instead of throwing it out on the highway or dumping it in the nearest convenient place. Everyone should think twice before cutting down a tree or breaking a flowering plant. And if a hornet blunders into your room, capture it gently using an inverted tumbler and a piece of cardboard slid between the glass and the window pane; and instead of crushing the insect, release it outdoors. It too enjoys the warmth and light of the sun, it too has only one life, and its time is measured as is yours. And though the difference between a man and a hornet may seem immense, it is only a difference of degree. Because, in fact, there is only one kind of life.

My little spider has caught a fly and is busy trussing it up with threads of silk. And it occurs to me as I watch this deft operation that, although I can clearly see the spider, the spider cannot see me. We live on levels so completely different that the denizens of the lower one do not even know that the higher one exists. And the disquieting idea occurs to me that, perhaps, there are levels still higher than mine, and that I too am watched by something so immensely big that it is forever outside my ken.

As a matter of fact, what proof do I have that mine is the highest level? Not very long ago man believed that the earth was the center of the universe. Then he found that it actually is nothing but a speck of dust in a galaxy so vast that it staggers the imagination. And today he knows that even this immense galaxy is only one of billions of similar galaxies that drift in space of such titanic dimensions that he had to invent the light-year to measure it. A light-year is the distance which light, traveling at a speed of some 186,000 miles per second, covers in one year—about six trillion miles. And today, man's horizon in space—the depth to which he has penetrated with the eyes of giant telescopes—lies two billion times six trillion miles away. Even then there is no indication of a limit to the universe.

Against the background of his universe, man appears smaller than a virus appears in relation to man. I can no more fathom the true nature of my universe than a virus swimming in the stream of my blood or living within a cell of my body can gauge the nature of its world.

Scientists have found that matter consists of atoms and that atoms consist of a nucleus surrounded by a cloud of electrons. They also have discovered that the structure of the atom is such that it consists mostly of empty space, since the distances between the components of the atom are relatively immense. If we imagine the nucleus of an atom to be the size of a cherry, its electrons could be represented by mosquitoes buzzing around in circles of more than a mile in diameter. Similarly, matter too is mostly empty space. The distances between neighboring atoms are relatively so vast that the "cherries" would be spaced hundreds of miles apart. If it were possible to squeeze all the empty space out of a man, his body would be reduced to a barely visible speck. And if one of the electrons whirling, planet-like, around the sun-like nucleus of a calcium atom in one of the cells of my bones were inhabited by subatomic beings, such beings, contemplating their subatomic universe would feel dwarfed just as I do, by the immensity of their "cosmic space." And the awesome thought comes to my mind—and recent investigations by astrophysicists of the so-called "quasi-stellar sources" or quasars, those mysterious emitters of immensely powerful radiation, seem to point in the same direction—that, since the atom and the universe seem to be organized along somewhat similar lines, perhaps still larger structures may exist, and that the solar system is nothing but an atom, and galaxies are nothing but molecules, in a superstructure of unfathomable dimensions.

At first, such a thought seems fantastic. Yet is it really more fantastic than the presently accepted cosmological theory according to which space has no boundaries, stops nowhere, and yet is finite? Or than the realization that the velocity of light appears the same to all investigators, regardless of whether they move toward or away from its source at no matter how high a speed; that light and electrons possess the properties both of a solid hard particle and a wave; that electron waves are not "real" waves but "waves of probability;" or that, in the final analysis, our bodies consist of "waves of probability" and empty space?

Toward the end of the last century, scientists were convinced that the universe was almost thoroughly explored; that they knew most of the answers to the problems of science; and that the few remaining mysteries were on the threshold of solution. Everything, they thought, could be explained in terms of Newtonian concepts of matter, gravitation, space, and time, and the great British physicist Lord Kelvin declared that he could understand nothing of which he could not make a working model.

Today, this mechanistic explanation of the universe, regarded as hopelessly inadequate, has been abandoned. Recent discoveries in atomic and subatomic physics and refinements in our methods of observation have disclosed vast number of phenomena which cannot possibly be explained in Newtonian terms. At a contemporary physicist's convention Lord Kelvin would have felt as inadequate as a high-school student.

Today the universe appears more mysterious than ever before. Each new discovery seems to raise more questions than it answers, opening vistas into new unimaginable realms. By now, our understanding of nature has reached a point where it is no longer possible to interpret scientific findings in common-sense terms. Trying to translate into mechanistic analogies related to everyday experience many of the mathematical formulas used today by scientists to describe complex physical phenomena is as futile as trying to recognize realistic objects in modern abstract paintings. The more we learn about the true nature of matter, space, and time, the more we realize how little we actually know. And slowly the recognition begins to dawn that, just as even the most intelligent of animals will never be able to understand (except, perhaps, on the most superficial level) the functions of man's creations, so man himself, despite his marvelous brain, may be congenitally unable ever to comprehend fully the nature of the universe.

I do not find this thought disturbing. Nor does it prevent me from pursuing my scientific interests. The fact that an ideal is unobtainable has never prevented man from pursuing it. We may never comprehend the ultimate truth; but we can approach it. And the key to its secrets is science, for the essence of science is the search for truth. Thanks to science, I know that the piece of rock lying on my table, with its delicate remains of animals long since extinct—crinoids, corals, and shells—is not the mute witness of an avenging flood which occurred only a few thousand years ago, as the Bible suggests, but is Devonian limestone which was formed some four hundred million years ago on the bottom of a warm and shallow sea. This is truth. And to me, truth is the one immutable rock in a sea of uncertainty and change. Because, like any other human being, I need the reassurance of something immutable. But to find this immutable something—and we still do not know what it is—man has to be free spiritually—free from taboos and superstition, free from dogmas laid down in fear and ignorance and never revised in the light of added insight; free to pursue the truth wherever the chase may lead. And I am sure—as sure as anyone can ever be of anything—that at the end there will be light, the all-pervading light of insight illuminating the entire immense structure of the cosmos, and with it revealing the rightful place and purpose of man.

New Milford, Connecticut

ANDREAS FEININGER

I

The Land

Nothing is permanent. Everything is in constant flux and change. Through day and night, through summer and winter, year after year, from birth to death, life flows in a timeless cycle—life in the soil and on the ground, in water and air, life of man and animal and plant—always in change and transformation, in rise and fall, in growth and decline, so that in all nature nothing is the same at day's end as it was at day's beginning.

And on a larger scale, more slowly yet just as relentlessly, the earth itself changes. Incessantly, irresistibly, the forces of nature carve the massive face of the land into new forms. The solid earth is not as solid as it seems. It has some kind of life of its own. It seethes with internal volcanic activity. It pulsates with the ocean tides. It heaves and subsides. Mountains are thrust up to craggy heights and worn down again into plains. The scale of this activity is immense, the time is measured in eons.

Abundant signs testify to this ceaseless change, the evidence is everywhere to see for those who care to look. Remnants of marine life—sea shells and the skeletons of fish—are found on mountaintops, testifying that those lofty heights once formed the bottom of an ocean. Holes drilled by stone-boring date mussels (*Lithophaga*) of a type still living in the nearby sea pockmark the columns of the Greek temple of Serapis at Pozzuoli near Naples. These holes are evidence of repeated vertical earth movements which once lowered the temple below the level of the sea and later lifted it out of the water again so smoothly that its columns remained upright. Coal has been found in arctic grounds, proving that these frozen wastes once had a warmer climate. And the grooves, ridges, and polished bedrocks that are the signature of grinding sheets of ice thousands of feet thick can still be seen in many now temperate lands, proof of enormous climatic and environmental changes.

Two titanic forces constantly sculpture the crust of the earth: diastrophism and erosion. The forces of diastrophism originate deep down in the earth's seething interior and take physical shape in the upthrust of mountains, in volcanic activities, and in the tilting, folding, fracturing, rising, and lowering of whole segments of the earth's crust. The effects of erosion are confined more or less to the surface of the land. Left to itself, each of these forces would change the character of the earth beyond recognition: rampant diastrophism would turn the land into a jagged nightmare world; unchecked erosion would eventually level the entire surface of the earth and smooth it into a plain evenly covered by water. Fortunately for mankind, an uneasy balance between diastrophism and erosion exists as a result of which we can have dry land and oceans, mountains and plains.

Erosion wears away the land by breaking down the rocks and transporting the debris from higher to lower places. Its main agencies are weathering—the effects of heat and cold, the chemical action of the components of the atmosphere on rock, and the mechanical action of wind and water—and gravity. Solar energy heats the rocks and, through differential expansion, produces minute cracks in the stone. Water penetrates into these cracks and freezes at night, splitting the stone as the ice expands. This opens up larger crevices in which wind-blown soil can accumulate, offering a first toe hold to the seedlings of trees whose growing roots further pry apart the stone. Oxygen and carbon dioxide from the air combine chemically with certain elements in the rocks, causing them to crumble and decay. Abrasive wind-borne sand grinds away at the rocks. Water leaches out the soluble components of stone. Lichen and rotting plants produce acids that further accelerate the processes of rock decay. Wind and rain carry small particles toward lower places where flooding streams complete the work of destruction by further grinding down the stony debris and sweeping the resulting mud and sand to still lower ground and finally out to sea. The scale at which erosion proceeds can be gathered from the fact that annually the Mississippi River alone carries over six hundred million tons of soil into the Gulf of Mexico, where, added to previously deposited sediments, it contributes to the buildup of the land.

To mankind, erosion is a two-sided phenomenon. Without erosion, there would be no soil, for soil is pulverized rock mixed with organic matter. Without soil, extensive plant life could not exist on land and without green plants there could be neither animals nor man. On the other hand, unless kept in check by favorable natural conditions or suitable artificial countermeasures, erosion also destroys what it creates. Wherever man does not take good care of his lifegiving soil he will lose it in cataclysmic dust storms and ravaging floods.

On the following pages are shown some of the forms and structures that result when land is torn down or built up.

1. A view of the Canadian Rockies near Lake Louise. Immense valley glaciers that vanished long ago carved these mountains into their present harsh and craggy configurations. At the left is Lake Louise, a typical "finger lake" gouged out by the main mass of the ice. It is bordered by large moraines now overgrown with spruce and fir. The two small "kettlehole lakes" or tarns are the vestiges of a smaller, secondary glacier. The nearby rocks have been shattered by frost action. "Hanging glaciers" covering the tops of the mountains in the background are the last remains of the receding ice.

2. Death Valley, California. The clean, wind-rippled sand of this tremendous dune was once solid granite high up in the nearby Cottonwood Mountains. Sheared away by heat and frost, leveled from their heights by rain and mountain streams, boulders, rocks, and mineral debris descend, collecting at the mountain's base and spilling out upon the floor of the valley in the form of great alluvial fans. There, in the blistering desert sun, the debris quickly dries and ceaseless winds pick up the pulverized material and pile it up into immense, constantly shifting dunes. The only signs of life are the tiny footprints of an insect, which, like a miniature railroad track, traverse the scorching sands.

3. Wind erosion in Death Valley, California. In arid regions where the soil is dry and vegetation sparse, wind is often the most powerful tool of erosion. In this picture, hummocks of arrow weed fight a ceaseless battle for survival, their straggling lateral roots trying to trap the wind-blown soil. Despite their hostile environment, most of these plants, adapted to arid conditions, succeed in growing upward, although the desert floor is gradually being eroded.

4. Red sandstone cliff in Zion National Park, Utah. The kind of erosion shown here, in which great slabs break away from the parent rock in the form of enormous arches, is typical of massive, unstratified rocks. Under certain conditions it leads to the formation of "natural bridges." The causes underlying this particular form of erosion are not yet fully understood.

5. El Capitan, Yosemite Valley, California. The massive dome which guards the entrance to this valley is a single monolith of white plutonic granite which was cut and polished by a vanished glacier. For a view which clearly shows the wide-bottomed, U-shaped cross-section typical of this and any other glacier-cut valley, turn to plate 41.

6—7. Alkali flat in Utah. Here we see what is one of the most desolate and barren stretches on earth. Heavy impregnation of the soil with sodium, potassium, borax, or gypsum makes it impossible for plants to grow except in a few isolated spots where leaching has reduced the salinity of the soil. The main cause of this high salinity is lack of rain, which normally would have dissolved the soluble surface minerals and drained them off deep into the ground.

8. A flood plain in Arizona. During one of the rare heavy flash floods typical of desert areas, a sheet of water causes surface dust to coagulate as mud. When the waters recede, this deposit dries and through loss of volume shrinks and cracks. This picture shows how land is built up by deposits of water-carried sands and clays. The cone-like structure on the horizon is the hard lava core of an extinct volcano whose covering of softer rocks has been worn away by erosion.

9. A crevasse in the ice of the Athabaska glacier, the second largest in the great Columbia ice field of the Canadian Rockies. In summer, melt-water makes tunnels and caverns in the ice which occasionally collapse, forming crevasses. The run-off from this glacier forms the source of the Athabaska River.

10. Granite erosion in Colorado. Weathering of massive rocks generally produces spheroidal (rounded) shapes. The large boulder just to the right of center clearly shows a form of erosion called exfoliation; it is characterized by large areas of the stony surface breaking off in flakes.

11. Erosion of marly clay in Utah. The towers and spires of the spectacular formations in Bryce Canyon were sculptured by rain and running water in a double process of leaching and abrasion. The pink color is caused by iron oxide (rust) which permeates the rock.

12. Various forms of erosion

Top left: Undercut by running water, this massive rock, which formed part of the bank of a stream, broke off because it lost its support. Now, water entering the cleft and freezing there will further accelerate its break-up into smaller parts.

Top right: Once a crack is large enough for soil to accumulate in it, the wedging power of the roots of trees growing in the cleft will pry it farther apart.

Bottom left: Rills in sandstone were gouged out by draining surface water which dissolved the limy cement that once bound the grains of sand together.

Bottom right: Close-up of a disintegrating sandstone boulder. Lichen growing on the stone produces acids which slowly eat into its surface, creating shallow depressions in which rainwater could collect. Subsequent leaching transformed these indentations into deep holes.

13. Various forms of erosion

Top left: Surface water percolating through porous limestone leached out its soluble parts and formed a deep cavity.

Top right: A "pedestal rock" in Utah. A capstone protected the top of this strange formation from the rain. Its lower parts, which consisted of softer materials—gravel and clay—were gradually washed away. Sooner or later, of course, the entire structure will collapse.

Bottom left: Thinly stratified rocks bordering a stream are eroded and polished by running water.

Bottom right: "Pot-holes" in the rocky bed of a creek are ground spherically by the scouring action of swirling water currents loaded with abrasive sand.

14—15. View across the Grand Canyon from the south rim. This immense chasm is one of the most spectacular sights on earth. It is the work of the Colorado River, which, at this point, is only about three hundred feet wide and thirty feet deep, has a volume of some twenty thousand cubic feet of water a second, and carries toward the Gulf of Mexico a daily load of some five hundred thousand tons of rock debris and soil. Geologically speaking, the Colorado is still a young and therefore fast-cutting river which, during the last ten million years, has gouged out of the Colorado Plateau a canyon which is now 217 miles long, eight to twenty miles wide, and more than a mile deep. At its present rate of cutting, the river is eating into the hard Precambrian rock and deepening its channel at the rate of five and one-half inches every thousand years. In this photograph, the river itself is barely visible at the extreme left edge of the picture. The blue tone is the result of atmospheric haze.

16. Millions of years ago, winds picked up the fine debris of still more ancient mountains leveled by erosion and in sifted layers deposited numberless grains of quartz to form this cross-bedded sandstone cliff. Now these very rocks are worn away by erosion's force, their change documenting the ceaseless cycle of construction and destruction that eternally runs through nature.

17. Bedded limestone cliff forming the canyon wall of the Little Colorado River. Like the pages of an immense book, these layers of Permian limestone, deposited some 250 million years ago in a process of accretion, contain nature's record of the passage of time. Here, the trained geologist can read the history of the earth.

1 ▶

◀2
3▶

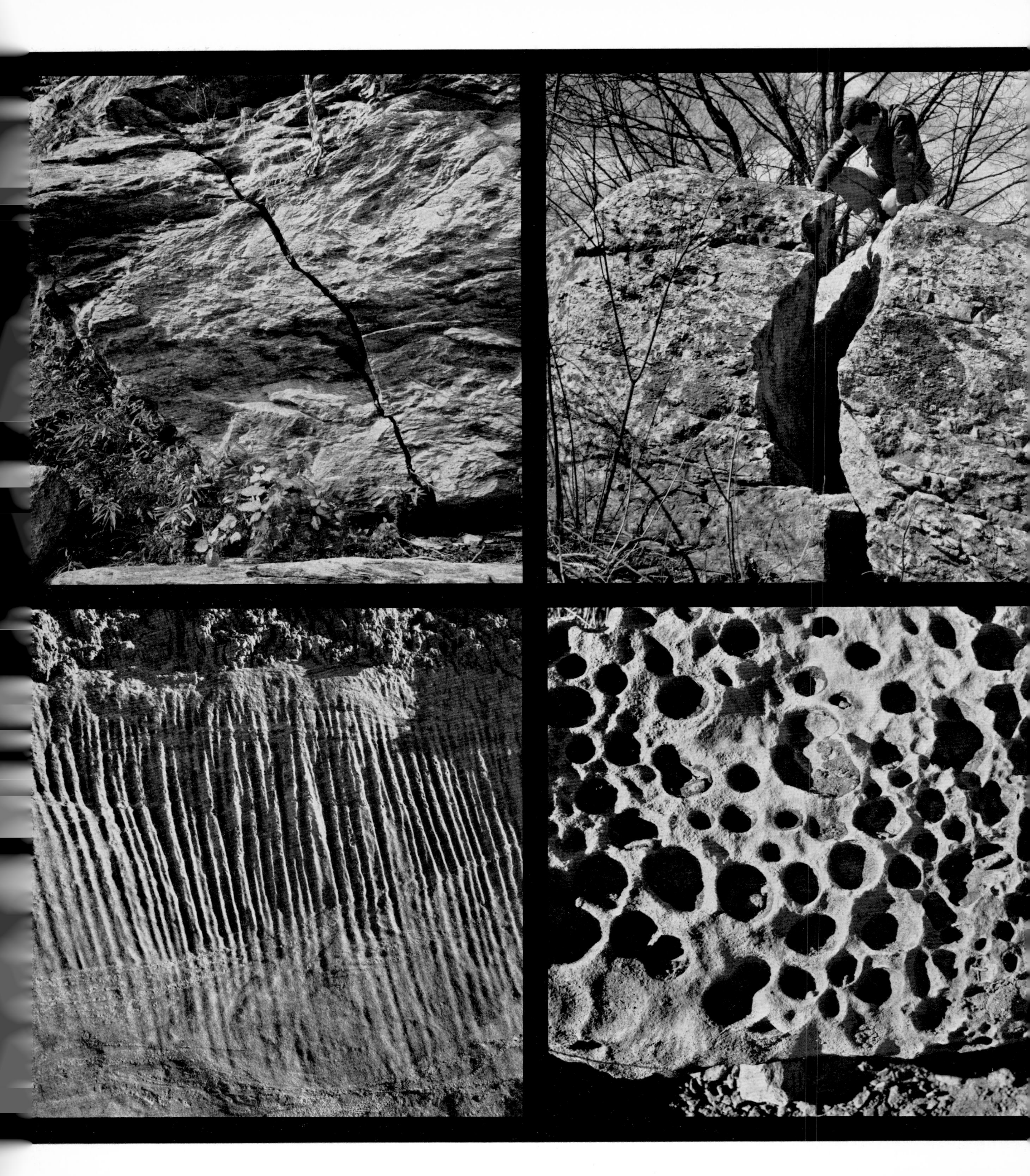

II

Erosion in Microscale

Eternally, all-pervading, the forces of erosion change and rechange the features of the land. These processes work on many scales from the largest to the smallest. In their more spectacular forms—a dust storm, a rampaging flood, a land-slide that carries away part of a village—they make headlines. In microscale—grains of sand dislodged by raindrops, hairline cracks opened up by frost in a rock, the destructive role which lichens play in breaking down a stone—they go largely unnoticed although their cumulative effect is just as consequential as that of the more spectacular phenomena. Given time enough—thousands and millions of years—even such minute phenomena as hairline cracks in rocks and the tiny splash of individual raindrops, multiplied trillionfold, are sufficient to wear down mountains, reduce their substance to dust, and level their soaring heights into plains. How some of these phenomena manifest themselves when seen from close up is shown on the following pages.

18. A close up of the floor of the Painted Desert in New Mexico. Stained a fantastic pink by mineral oxides, scorched by searing desert winds, its mud coating crazed by drought and heat, this product of erosion presents a picture of sterility and desolation in which the bleached skull of a cow assumes almost symbolic significance.

19. Lichen on a rock in Connecticut. Where no other form of plant life can exist, lichens, because of their unique nature, may still be able to grow. Lichens are composite organisms consisting of two totally unrelated kinds of plants, an alga and a fungus, joined in inseparable partnership, the alga providing the fungus with organic nutrients made by photosynthesis from air and water while the fungus, able to produce an acid which dissolves stone, provides the alga with the necessary minerals without which it cannot exist. As a result, lichens are always the first plants to settle on barren ground. As they proliferate, they break down the stone and leave it open to further attack by the forces of water and frost, thus starting the process of soil formation and preparing the way for higher forms of plant life to follow.

20—21. Eroded clay bank. As evident from the photograph at the bottom of plate 20, the actual extent of this "landscape" is very small; the barbed-wire fence in the background reveals its real size. However, seen from nearby, small segments of this miniature scene—except, of course, for scale—are virtually identical with actual landscapes of a kind typical of the arid American Southwest. In the scaleless pictures (plate 20 top, and plate 21), features which in reality were only inches high, assume the appearance of deeply eroded canyons cut by rapid mountain creeks, grass and weeds become trees, and the rivulets of dried mud bring to mind the fantastically eroded limestone pinnacles of Bryce Canyon (plate 11).—All of which goes to show that, basically, the manifestations of erosion are the same no matter what their scale.

22—23. Erosion manifested on the smallest scale. These pictures show depositions of river mud cut away by erosion. Here, drops of rain have swept away sand grains and particles of clay, etching the mud with fine erosive lines. And although these patterns in reality cover areas only inches wide—the phenomena are here depicted in more than natural size—aerial photographs of eroded mountains often show features that are virtually identical. The forces which created these small patterns, multiplied billions of times, incessantly change the surface of the land.

24. Water-deposited mud dries in concave broken-saucer shapes, their edges revealing their layered

◀ 18

structure. Shrinkage produces polygons; a faster rate of drying on their surfaces produces the curl.

25. When drying in broken flakes that look like wood shavings, a thin coat of water-deposited mud, rain-spotted, peels like weathered paint.

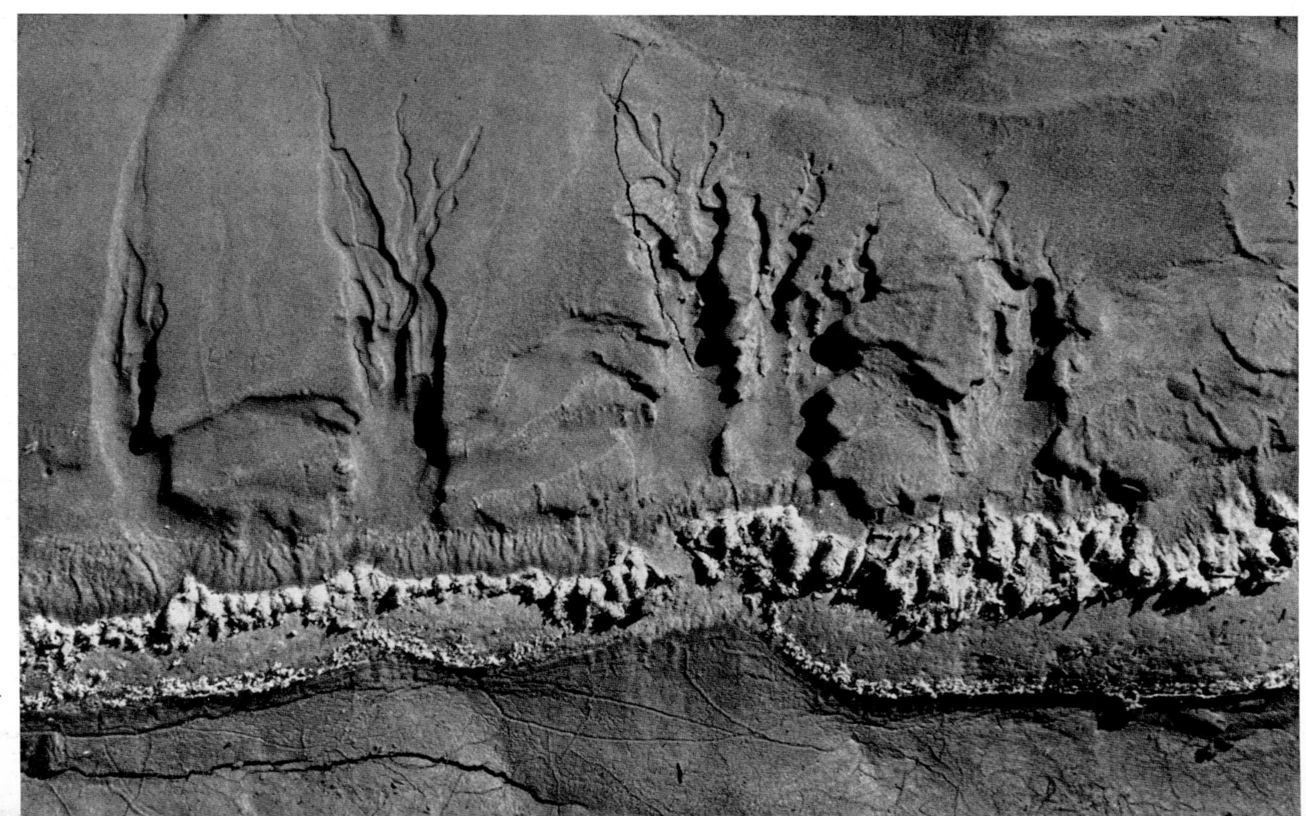

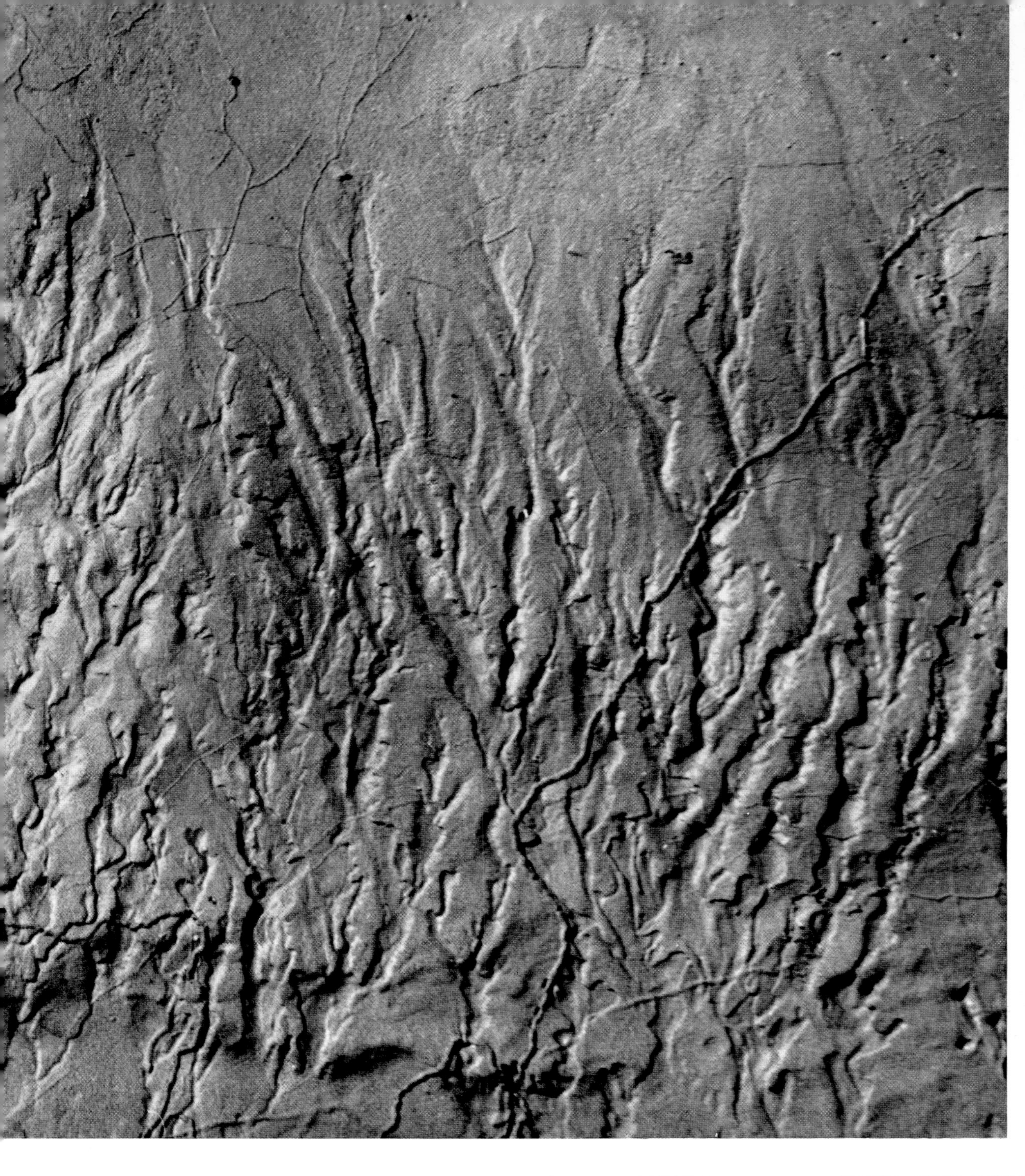

5

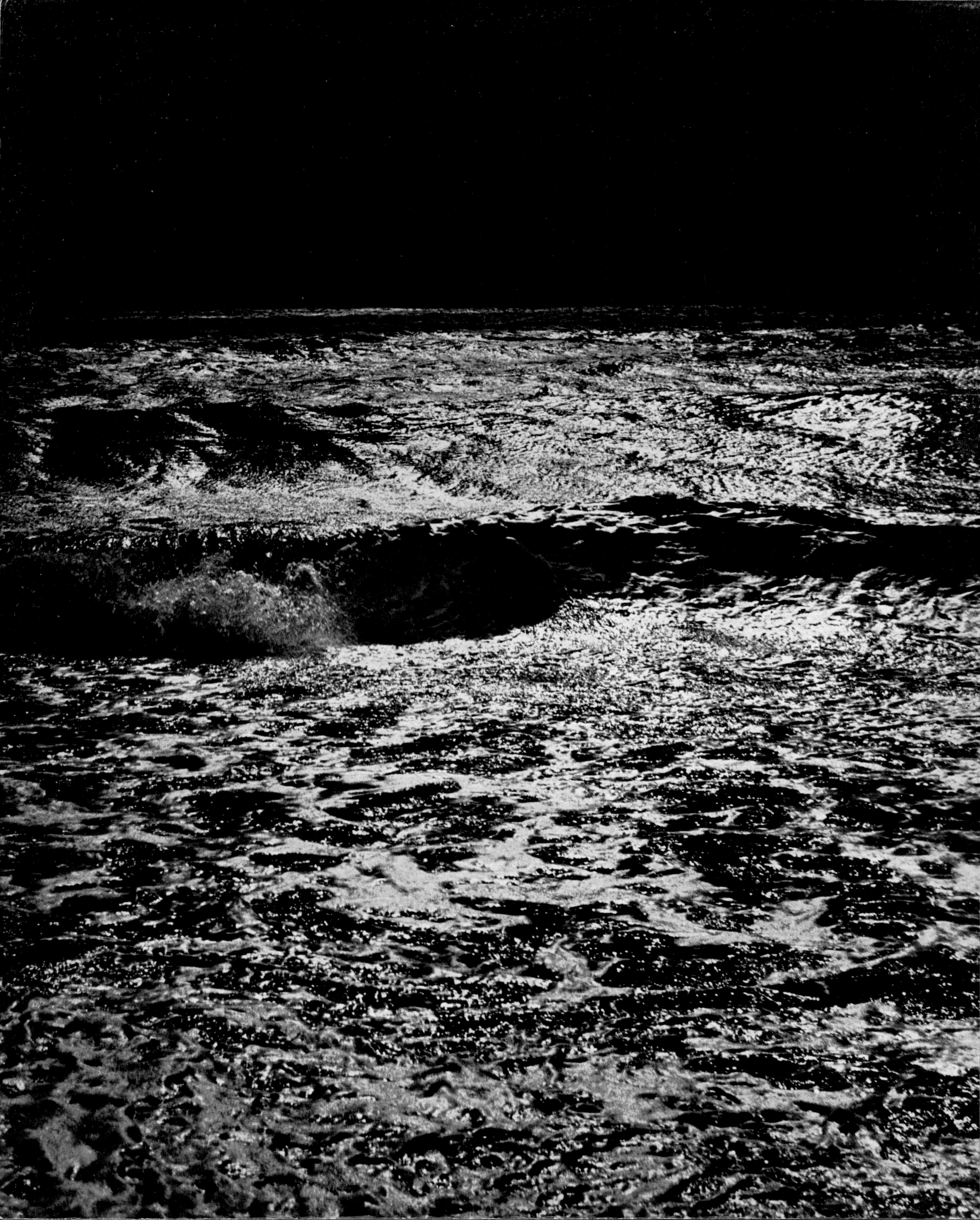

III

The Water

Water is perhaps the most powerful and destructive and, as far as life is concerned, the most indispensable, single force on earth. Without water, our world would be devoid of life and its crust would be as jagged as the surface of the moon.

Water in the liquid state seems to be an extremely rare and almost unique occurrence within the universe. Most heavenly bodies either are flaming spheres of incandescent gas or drift through the abysmal cold of interstellar space in an eternally frozen state. And among our sister planets, as far as we know, none contains water in liquid form, although small amounts of moisture in the form of hoarfrost and dew probably on Mars. The reason for this scarcity is that water can occur in liquid form only within an extremely narrow band of the multi-million-degree temperature spectrum of the universe. And it is only within this hairline temperature range that life as we know it can exist.

This is so because all forms of life are largely made of water. The human body, for example, consists of approximately 70 per cent water, one-third of which is used in the making of the blood and other body fluids, two-thirds to build the protoplasm within the cells. And it is a thought-provoking and deeply significant fact that the chemical constituents of our blood are the same as those of sea water—although the proportions are slightly different—a fact which tends to confirm the belief of scientists that life originated in the sea.

But not only is water in its liquid form a substance of great rarity in the universe; it also holds a unique position here on earth insofar as it possesses an extraordinary property; unlike most other liquids and solids, which contract as they cool, water, when it freezes, expands in volume by 9 per cent. This extraordinary behavior is infinitely more than merely a curious anomaly of interest only to scientists; it is a quality without which our climate would be vastly different. Filling a larger volume than its original amount of water, ice is lighter than water and therefore floats. If this were not so, ice would sink as fast as it was formed and large parts of the oceans would be frozen from the bottom up. This, of course, would severely restrict if not altogether stop, with subsequent drastic consequences for life, the flow of the Gulf Stream and other oceanic currents which, by their ceaseless transfer of hot and cold water masses, contribute so much to the tempering and stabilization of our climate.

Another remarkable quality of water is its capacity for storing heat, in which it is surpassed by no other liquid or solid except ammonia. As a result, the oceans are able to play the role of vast storehouses of solar energy, contributing to the preservation of climatic stability.

And finally, water is a versatile solvent. This quality has a twofold effect: on the one hand, water erodes the ground by leaching its minerals and contributes to the disintegration of rocks by dissolving some of their components; on the other hand, by depositing these mineral solutions in the sea, it constantly enriches the mineral content of the oceans and makes them veritable storehouses of nutrients for plankton, those minute organisms which support all animal life in the sea, and therefore help to increase the food reserves of man.

Among the many forces of erosion, running water is the most powerful. Every year an estimated one hundred thousand cubic miles of water evaporates into the atmosphere and falls back upon the earth as rain, snow, sleet, or hail. And although the larger part of this unimaginable volume falls back into the sea, some thirty thousand cubic miles of moisture come down upon the land. Much of this precipitation, of course, disappears underground or evaporates before it can be

◀ 26

utilized by life or participate in the erosion of the land. But there remain an estimated ten million billion gallons annually which will run off and eventually reach the sea as surface water. It is this water which plays such an important role in sculpturing the land.

26. The sea off Cape Cod, Massachusetts, photographed under a lowering sky. Seventy-one per cent of the earth is covered by salt water. The average ocean depth is ten thousand feet, the combined volume of all the seas is roughly three hundred million cubic miles. How enormous a reservoir of salt water this represents can be gathered by the fact that if all the mountains and valleys on earth were leveled and the globe made into a perfectly smooth sphere, the sea would uniformly cover its entire surface to a depth of eight thousand feet. And if all the water that is now locked up in the form of ice and snow—the polar icecaps and the glaciers and snowfields of mountain areas—were suddenly to melt, the present sea level would rise one hundred and fifty to two hundred feet and most of the big cities of the world would be under water.

27. The first few hundred feet of the Hudson River near the top of Mount Marcy in the Adirondacks, New York State. Rain falling on a wooded watershed percolates through layers of humus, gathers to rivulets, and forms the beginning of a stream, picking up large amounts of carbonic acid from decaying organic matter in the process. If this acid-laden water flows over or percolates through rock formations which contain limestone, it leaches out the lime, which it carries away in the form of calcium carbonate solution. The effect of such leaching is twofold: tunnels and underground caves will be formed which, if close enough to the surface, may in time collapse, forming sinkholes; the famous Carlsbad Caverns in New Mexico and the Luray Cave in Virginia, for example, are produced by leaching. On the other hand, the water may again precipitate its load of lime drop by drop somewhere else in the form of "dripstone"—the stately stalagmites that grow upward from the floor of many caves, and the spiky stalactites that grow downward from their roofs.

28. Rain. The erosive action of rain is partly chemical and partly mechanical. Not only is water, as mentioned before, in itself an excellent solvent capable of decomposing many minerals, but in their fall from the clouds to the ground, the drops of rain inevitably absorb some carbon dioxide from the air. As a result, they turn into weak acids and therefore become chemically more aggressive and erosively more powerful, particularly in their effect on limestone and lime-containing forms of rock and soil, which they corrode through leaching. In limestone country, this can have the undesirable consequence that rain water quickly penetrates the ground and collects in underground channels formed by leaching, which prevents the formation of surface streams and promotes desert-like conditions.

The mechanical action of rain is, of course, limited mainly to the washing away of the finer particles of the soil. Unfortunately, these particles are most necessary to the healthy growth of plants. Once they are gone, the vegetable ground cover will decrease; fewer roots will be available to hold the soil together and fewer leaves to break the force of falling rain. The less well-protected land will be more vulnerable to the onslaught of rain, gullying will set in, and the productivity of the land will go down and may be entirely lost.

29. Moosehead Lake, Maine. Lakes like this are valuable reservoirs which ensure a steady year-round supply of water because, like an enormous sponge, their marshy shores and heavily wooded surroundings absorb the drenching rains and masses of melting snow, releasing the water gradually over a period of time and thus preventing sudden, dangerously fast run-offs with subsequent floods which would damage the land. In addition, they provide food and shelter for a rich variety of wildlife and recreation in the form of fishing, boating, and swimming.

30. Ice feathers on a window pane, shown here at approximately twelve times their natural size. The remarkable resemblance between these crystalline structures and certain types of ferns and feathers, and also the leaves of the Ginkgo tree, will intrigue the inquiring mind.

31. A pond in the process of freezing, photographed at the moment when water changes from the liquid to the solid state. Still floating freely on the surface in a paper-thin layer, the individual ice crystals align themselves in regular patterns that resemble enormous plumes, soon to fuse and harden into a solid sheet of ice.

32. Jacks Fork River in Missouri's Ozark Mountains. With any curving stream, the eroding effect is always stronger on the outside of the curve than on the inside. This shows clearly in this photograph, which was made from the top of the limestone bluff into which the river had cut its bed, eroding its outer banks and wearing them down through undercutting and abrasion while at the same time adding material to the gravel banks that line the inside of the bend.

33. The upper valley of the Yosemite River in Wyoming. This is a typical example of the erosive effect of a, geologically speaking, "young," swift-flowing stream. Such a stream usually starts on some mountainside from a number of gulleys fed by run-off water. Theoretically, its channel might be an increasingly deeper chasm with nearly vertical sides. In reality, however, this channel is usually more or less V-shaped in cross-section because, as the stream grinds away at the bottom, the sides are constantly worn back by the action of rain, frost, gravity, and other erosive agents which produce greater or lesser slides, break down the rims, and thereby widen the chasm. The cutting power of running water is approximately equivalent to the square of its velocity. Thus the erosive force of a stream flowing at a speed of three miles an hour is roughly nine times as great as that of a stream flowing at only one mile an hour. It is mainly because of this that rivers are most destructive in times of flood when their velocities reach a peak.

34—35. Lake Tear in the Clouds near the top of Mount Marcy in the Adirondacks, New York State. Hidden deep in the heart of the watershed and fed by the run-off from the encircling mountains, this fog-shrouded bog is the source of the mighty Hudson River. Immense forests surround it, their numberless trees protecting the ground from the onslaught of the elements. While alive, their deeply tangled roots firmly hold the soil; when dying and decaying, they add their substance to the ever-growing layer of humus, the marvelous material which, porous and resilient, like an enormous mountain-blanketing sponge, absorbs the fury of drenching rains and the flood waters of melting snow and releases their moisture all year round.

36. Dewdrops caught in a spider web. During a chilly autumn night, falling temperature precipitated moisture out of the cooling air to form these jewel-like, sparkling drops.

37. Buttercups flooded by the rising Mississippi River. Spring is the time when life-giving rains irrigate the land, a time of both hope and fear—hope that the waters may promote growth, fear that flood-swollen rivers may break from their channels and wash away the soil or bury rich farm land under choking layers of silt.

38. A geyser in Yellowstone National Park. Resembling a volcano in miniature, this vent blowing off clouds of billowing steam testifies to the seething fury that reigns in the earth's interior. Minerals precipited layer by layer out of the scalding solutions which welled up from the deep and overflowed its rim built this volcano-like cone.

39. Under a canopy of alto-cumulus clouds, black vultures soar above the New Mexican desert. Clouds consist of minute droplets of water or microscopic crystals of ice condensed in the atmo-

sphere from water which, under the influence of solar heat, had evaporated from the earth. Water vapor is a relatively rare gas—if the total amount contained in the atmosphere were to precipitate, the resulting layer of water would cover the globe to a depth of only one inch. Yet despite its sparseness, water vapor is a vitally important constituent of the atmosphere. Without it, there would be no changing weather, no rain, and no land-life as we know it. Furthermore, because of its ability to absorb and store heat, water vapor plays an important role in maintaining the temperature balance on which all life depends. Without water vapor, unmitigated solar radiation would scorch the earth during the day, while at night heat would radiate back into space unchecked, and freezing cold would bite deeply into the dust-dry, unprotected ground.

40. Angel Glacier in the Canadian Rockies. Wherever perpetual snow exists, glaciers may form, for every glacier began as a snow field which, during long periods of heavy snow fall, became so deep that its own weight compacted its lower strata into ice. As its mass increases, the growing glacier will gradually begin to creep downward under its own weight, for ice, although a crystalline solid, nevertheless deforms under stress like a plastic. The daily rate of creep can range from fractions of an inch to as much as forty feet. However, compared to the enormous glaciers of the past, modern glaciers are relatively small and, because the mean temperature of the earth is rising, many glaciers, instead of advancing, are actually retreating and a number of them will disappear within our time. The actual size of Angel Glacier can be gauged by comparing it with the group of people which stand on the edge of the snow in the lower left-hand corner of the picture.

41. The entrance to Yosemite Valley in California. We see here a typical glacier-carved valley, characterized by a U-shaped cross-section with a wide, flat bottom and relatively steep sides. Whereas running water always follows the line of least resistance and streams therefore tend to cut valleys with interlocking spurs as shown in plate 33, a valley glacier does not, as a rule, swing from side to side but plows a relatively straight furrow. It derives its erosive power from a combination of bulldozing, scraping, and tearing. The front of the moving ice mass digs into the valley ground and pushes loose soil and rocks ahead of it. At the same time, rocks frozen into the bottom and the sides of the glacier, acting like the diamonds of a grinding wheel, scrape through the floor and the sides of the valley, grooving, scouring, and polishing the bedrock underneath. And finally, ice that has frozen to the mountain tears away large hunks of rock whenever the glacier moves.

27 ▶

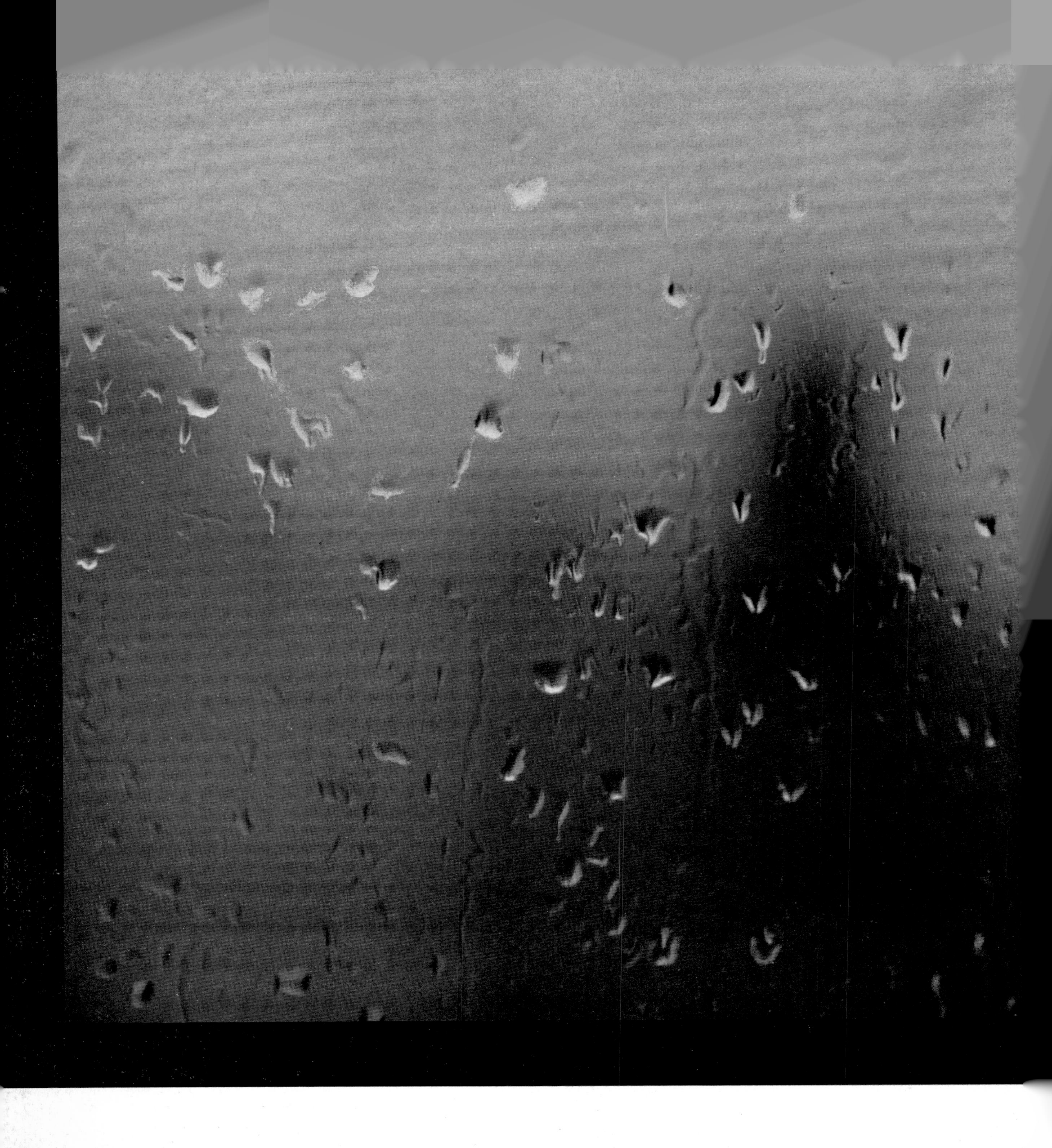

◀ 32
33 ▶

◀ 34/35 36-39 ▶

◀ 40
41 ▶

IV

The Shore

Wherever land and water meet, changes are likely to occur. This can be seen on every scale from the smallest to the largest, from the effect of raindrops on grains of sand or clods of soil to the action of the sea upon the edge of a continent. As a result of this eternal conflict between land and water, no shore line on earth is permanent, and what was said earlier holds true here too: no beach, headland, or coastal cliff anywhere on earth is the same at day's end as it was at day's beginning.

A shore line changes in two ways: either new land emerges from the sea or existing land is destroyed. Emergence of new land occurs primarily along shore lines where the forces of diastrophism have lifted the land until the gentle slope of the continental shelf itself is exposed. There, wave action tends to deposit more material than it tears away, with the result that protective sandbars accumulate, behind which tidal marshes form. And as the new land grows through accretion, the sea recedes, a process which can be observed along the southeastern coast of the United States, where it created wide sandy beaches from Cape Hatteras to the tip of Florida.

Destruction of the land occurs primarily along those shores where the rim of the continent is sinking and the mass of the land itself becomes exposed to attacks by the sea. There, where no gentle slopes break their force, the waves assault the shore like battering rams, undermining cliffs until the rocks come tumbling down and, shattered into fragments easily lifted by the surf, reinforce with their debris the power of the charging sea. How enormous this power can be is seen by the fact that big waves exert pressures of up to three tons per square foot. In some parts of the world rocky shore lines recede at the rate of twenty to thirty feet a year. Testimony to the destructive power of the sea are the rocky shores of Maine and Scotland and the towering cliffs of Dover and Calais.

42. The Pacific coast, south of San Francisco. Differential erosion by the sea wore down the soft-clay hills at a faster rate than the hard-rock headlands and resulted in the formation of a series of U-shaped bays where, in relatively quiet water, sand and gravel could accumulate. The size of these formations can be gauged by comparing them with the tiny figure of a man near the center of the left edge of the picture. Fog banks, as seen here, often appear along this coast.

43. Ripple marks in sand and stone. The rippled surface structure of wind-blown sand, plastic mud, or water is caused by oscillatory response to bouncing by wind or currents of water.

Top left and right: Aeolian (wind-formed) ripple marks give texture to these sand dunes in California's Death Valley. Contrary to popular belief, sand dunes are not confined to the vicinity of water but often occur in arid areas far from the sea.

Center left and right: Sliced by running water, these sectioned sand dunes bordering the Colorado River, showing both internal ripple marks and the effects of cross-bedding of the same kind that can be seen in fossil form in plate 16, reveal that sand dunes are not simply piles of sand. They possess, as a result of growth through accretion by wind action, a complex internal structure.

Bottom left: Hardened into stone, these fossil ripple marks are probably thousands of years old. The fact that they are identical with the ripple marks shown at the right proves that these sandstone formations originated as sediments deposited in shallow water.

Bottom right: The imprint of water's rippled flow retained in plastic river mud in a shallow backwater of the Colorado River.

44—45. Driftwood piled up on a Cape Cod beach. These are the stumps and roots of trees which

◀ 42

toppled into the sea when undercut parts of the coast collapsed. Battered and broken, scoured by sand and sea, cast up on the shore by the waves and bleached satin-silver by the sun, these derelicts delight the eye by their bizarre forms.

46. *Top:* Unsorted glacial till deposited by melting ice some twenty thousand years ago came to light when a modern highway was cut through an ancient moraine. Each rock and pebble has been ground into a spheroidal shape by the action of moving water and ice.

Bottom: An assortment of pebbles from Montauk Point beach, Long Island, New York. Years of grinding against one another in the surf, augmented by the scouring and polishing action of sand, has given these wave-tossed granite and quartz pebbles geometrically pure ellipsoidal forms.

47. A shingle beach at Montauk Point, Long Island, New York. Remnant of the last ice-age when it marked the farthest advance of a glacier, a moraine spills rock debris upon the beach as it collapses piecemeal under the ceaseless onslaught by the sea. Protected by headlands consisting of harder, material, a U-shaped cove is formed where pounding waves grind these pebbles into smaller and smaller pieces of increasingly regular elliptic shapes, ultimately to be pulverized by the surf into sand.

48—49. An aspect of the rocky coast near Middletown, Rhode Island. Known as stretch-pebble conglomerate, the individual stones had been highly metamorphosed by intense pressure and heat before tectonic forces lifted these formations from the deep. As a result, each pebble has been not only elongated but also shaped to conform to the contours of its neighbors. This can be clearly seen in plate 48, center right. It is interesting that when the entire mass breaks at right angles to the long axis of the individual stones (plate 48, bottom left), the resulting crack forms a perfectly flat plane because the tightly cemented pebbles behave as a solid mass of rock. Surface weathering, by dissolving the binding cement, reveals the shape of each stone and gives an idea of the enormous forces within the earth which squeezed pieces of rock into elongated shapes.

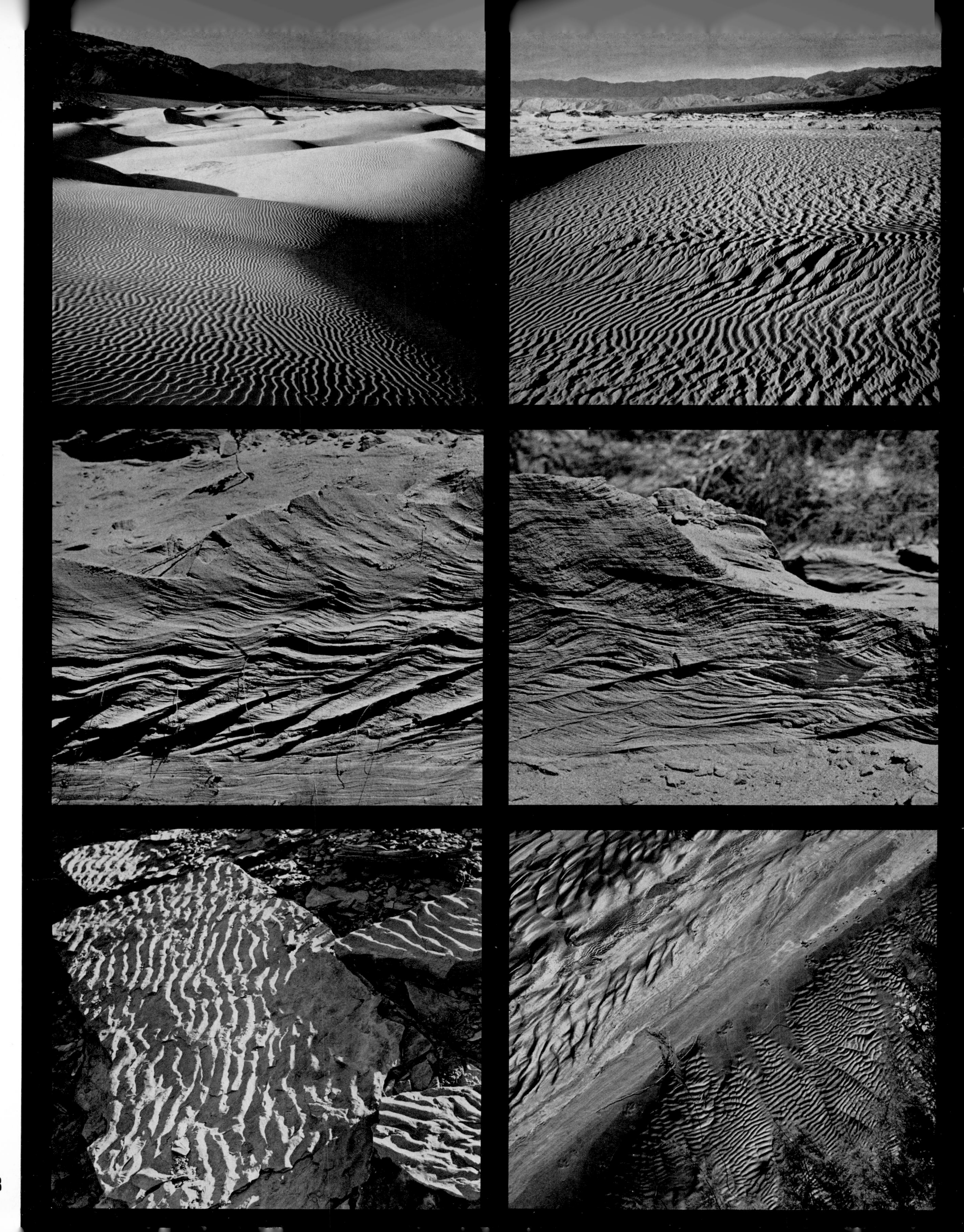

◀ 46
47 ▶

◀ 48

49

V

Animal Engineering

Man is not the only architect and engineer on earth. A large number of animals, from mammals and birds down to insects, spiders, and others still lower on the evolutionary ladder, build structures which, considering the size and equipment of their builders, are as interesting, beautiful, and worthy of admiration as New York's Verrazano Bridge or the Taj Mahal.

A great variety of different materials are used by these animals for their constructions. Many, like beavers, birds, or ants, collect material readily available in field or forest and use it more or less as they find it—mud and earth, sticks and branches, leaves and grass, hair and feathers shed by other animals—although the things they make out of this common stuff are often so intricate or beautiful that it is hard to believe they were made without benefit of reason, blueprints, or tools. Or the animal fabricates its own building material like the paper wasps, for example, which chew wood and bark into a pulp which they mix with their saliva to make the tough gray or brown paper they use to build their nests; certain tropical termites combine particles of soil with their saliva or intestinal fluids to form a cement which hardens into a stonelike mass and makes their huge mounds virtually invulnerable except to pickax or dynamite. And finally there are animals that produce their building material internally, through secretion, like the tent caterpillars, webworms, and spiders, which use silk to fashion their homes or snares.

Animals build their structures according to a powerful and orderly instinct. Their knowledge is part of their inheritance and will be passed on to the next generation in the same way; no parent ever taught a young bird how to construct a nest, or a spiderling how to lay out a web. As a result, they never vary a pattern and seldom make mistakes. Long before man existed, beavers constructed dams and practiced flood control, cliff swallows built homes of clay, like pottery, and certain types of termites air-conditioned their city states. Long before Euclid, spiders instinctively knew how to divide a circle into a large number of equal parts and hornets and bees had discovered that, in order to pack the largest number of the most useful type of cells most economically into the smallest amount of space, their cross-section must be hexagonal.

But perhaps even more astonishing and admirable than the strictly technical achievements of certain animals are the principles which underlie some of their constructions and the reasons why these were built as they are, although, in this context, it would be a great mistake to use the word "reason" in the usual sense.

Although they are able to learn, animals normally don't "reason"—they instinctively know. This form of "knowledge" is the same unreasoning prompting to action which makes our heart pump blood, our stomach digest food, and our gall bladder secrete bile—incredibly complex functions which our bodies perform although often we are not aware of them and do not "know" exactly how we do it. As a matter of fact, many animals instinctively know things which it took man thousands of years to learn, and even things which he still understands only imperfectly or not at all, despite all his efforts and experiments to find out.

For example, beaver installations in high and narrow mountain valleys are such perfect means of flood control that when farmers in lower regions, grudging the beavers their steady water supply, which they wished to use themselves to irrigate their fields, killed the beavers and destroyed their dams, they found to their dismay that by this thoughtless act they had only initiated a series of calamities: sudden flash floods which gullied the slopes and ripped away the soil alternated with periods of drought, so that they either had too much or too little water. And eventually, realizing their mistake and bowing to the superior knowledge of the beavers in matters of water regulation, they had to import a new family of beavers and settle them in the old location in order to save their land.

A fascinating "technology" has been developed by the incubator birds or mound builders (the family *Megapodidae*), birds the size of large hens or small turkeys, whose species range from Australia to Malaya and the Philippines. Unlike most other birds, these birds do not incubate their eggs with heat produced by the parent's body but instead have learned to harness for incubation purposes three forms of natural heat: solar radiation, the heat generated by decomposing vegetable matter, and volcanic heat. An explanation of this strange adaptive behavior is difficult to find, particularly in view of the fact that some of these forms of incubation involve an extraordinary amount of work for the birds. This is particularly true of the scrub fowl, an incubator bird which constructs huge "breeding mounds" five to fifteen feet high and twenty to thirty feet in diameter at the base. These mounds are made of vegetable debris which the birds rake together by scraping backward with their powerful feet, working from the periphery toward the center and throwing the litter toward the steadily accumulating heap. Gradually, the finished pile of rotting vegetable matter, in the manner of a compost heap, begins to generate heat, and when its internal temperature reaches 95 to 96 degrees Fahrenheit, the female, which has an extraordinarily well developed sense of heat, excavates a deep hole near the top of the pile, at the bottom of which she lays her eggs. Then she closes the hole again and leaves the eggs in the mound until they hatch. However, matters are even more complicated, because the temperature of the mound's interior must never vary more than one or two degrees or the eggs will perish. Therefore, when the sun is heating the mound, the birds, which have the sensitivity of a thermostat and are able to detect even minute fluctuations in heat, open vent holes in the side of the pile to aerate the heap; and when night falls and the temperature goes down, they pile up additional litter to keep the eggs at the constant temperature which their development demands. Since the incubation period may be as long as two months, this tiresome vigil goes on day and night, the birds ceaselessly tending their pile and, despite all outward fluctuations, keeping its interior temperature constant with a precision that is surpassed only by man's most sophisticated instruments. Other members of the mound builders' family have discovered that black volcanic sand, which gets hotter in the sun than ordinary white or yellow sand because of its black heat-absorbing color, is a better building material for incubators, and at breeding time these birds migrate long distances from their normal habitats to the relatively few areas where this desirable type of sand is found. Still other incubator birds lay their eggs in pits dug in ground which is warmed by subterranean steam in regions of volcanic activity, making use of the earth's internal heat.

Some of the most fascinating works by insects are the so-called compass mounds of certain Australian termites. These are huge slablike structures up to twelve feet high and ten feet long but only three to four feet thick, which—and this is the interesting feature—are almost invariably oriented so that their wide sides face east and west while their narrow edges point north and south. A tentative explanation of this peculiarity (how do these insects distinguish between the different points of the compass?) is that it has something to do with maintaining a uniform temperature within the nest, but this has not yet been proved.

What is known, however, is that certain African termites have invented a highly efficient ventilation system to aerate their huge conical city-mounds. Far from being simple honeycombed piles like structures, built of a cementlike material prepared by the termites from mud, possess a complex and orderly system of thin-walled, vertical ventilation ducts incorporated into the massive outside walls of the nest. The entrance and exit openings of these ducts connect with the central living quarters of the termites, and as the air warmed by the teeming masses of insects rises, it enters a dome-shaped chamber at the top of the nest and passes from there into the porous ventilation ducts. There, an interchange between inside and outside air takes place, in the process of which hot inside air, rich in suffocating carbon dioxide, is replaced by cool, oxygenated outside air, which enters the nest at the bottom of the mound, to be circulated again.

But one does not have to travel to the far corners of the earth to find marvels of animal engineering. And although the works of domestic species are generally less spectacular in regard to size than those of tropical forms, when closely examined they are no less thought-provoking. All the structures shown in the following pictures are the work of common species of animals which can be found almost anywhere in the United States by anyone who cares to look.

50—51. The work of the beaver. Beavers are best known for their pelts and their dams. Generally less well known is the purpose for which their dams are built: to create artificially the kind of environment that satisfies best the biological needs of these animals. Beavers are gregarious, relatively defenseless vegetarians that live in small colonies. They need protection from predators, an adequate year-round supply of food (they do not hibernate), and shelter in which to rear their young and survive the rigors of winter. The dam provides the means to satisfy these needs. By backing up a creek or stream it ensures an adequate, year-round supply of water sufficient to form a pond—large enough to enable the beavers to build their lodge at a safe distance from the shore where it is out of reach of marauders yet easily accessible to these strong swimmers; deep enough—from six to eight feet—so that it will not freeze solidly in winter but permit the beavers to use the underwater exit from their lodge and reach their stock pile of winter food—a heap of aspen, poplar, or willow branches, whose bark these animals eat. In addition, the pond provides an excellent environment for the growth of water lilies, whose pads and roots are the beavers' favorite summer food.

To create their domain and to keep it a going concern makes endless work for the beavers (hence the appropriateness of the saying "working like a beaver"). It involves the building of a beautifully engineered and integrated network of larger and smaller dams, canals and tunnels. The canals are sometimes several hundred feet long, so that logs can float in when the nearby supply of suitable food trees gives out. Constant repairs are necessary to keep the dikes watertight and sufficiently high and to maintain the lodge, a solidly constructed structure built of branches and the trunks of smaller trees plastered and made watertight with mud. Like a castle surrounded by its moat, the lodge is the focal point of the entire beaver colony, the place where the young are born and reared and the spot to which the members of the group retire in winter. It contains a single chamber some five feet wide and three feet high with an air hole in the ceiling and an underwater exit to the pond.

50. Detail of a beaver dam in the Rocky Mountains, Colorado.

51. *Top left:* An aspen gnawed halfway through by a beaver. To fell an aspen or a poplar four inches thick takes a fully grown beaver less than a quarter of an hour. But contrary to popular belief, beavers cannot make a tree fall in a desired direction.

Center left: The master builder himself.

Center right: Close-up of the lodge, which, in this colony, was located on a small island in the center of a system of different ponds.

The other pictures in plate 51 show structural details of different dams constructed of mud, grass sods, and sticks.

52. A colony of cliff swallows *(Petrochelidon pyrrhonota)* have built their pottery-like nests in the shelter of an overhanging bluff in Utah. Each nest is constructed of a large number of individual pellets of mud and forms a thin-walled shell, as can be clearly seen in this picture. These are the same birds as the famous swallows of the Mission of San Juan Capistrano in California. But contrary to a widespread belief, these swallows do return on the same day each year.

53. Nest of the ruby-throat hummingbird (*Archilochus colubris*). Many hummingbirds stick bits of lichen and moss, vegetable down, and pieces of spiderweb to the outside of their nests for camouflage. As a result, the nests usually blend so well with their surrounding that they become virtually invisible. I completely missed seeing this nest (which was shown to me by a professional ornithologist), although it was right under my nose.

54—55. Ant hills. Ants are probably the most widely spread, successful, and socially developed insects. The great cities of the mound builders can contain from forty thousand to a quarter of a million inhabitants under the rule of one to six or more queens. The mounds, which may reach up to five feet in height and be ten to twelve feet in diameter at the base, are skillfully constructed of bits of soil and clay, pine needles, and twigs, and are thatched and drained to keep the inside dry under all weather conditions. The picture at the left shows an ant hill in Colorado, surrounded by a zone which the ants keep bare of vegetation. The sectioned mound is the work of the wood ant (*Formica rufa*) and was found in Pennsylvania. To make this photograph, I sliced away part of the mound and covered the exposed side with a sheet of glass painted black on the outside. Then I waited until the ants had repaired the damage done to their home, removed the glass, and made the picture.

56. An ant lion pit. Ant lions (the family Myrmeleontidae)—the larvae of a graceful dragonfly-like insect (*Euroleon europaeus*)—have a great voracity for ants and other small arthropods. To capture these delicacies, the lion digs a conical pit two to three inches wide in loose soil or sand and buries itself at the bottom until only its wide-spread, pincer-like, needle-sharp jaws stick out. Then it waits patiently for ants to fall into its maws.

Excavating this pit is a surprisingly fast operation: shuffling backward in small circles, the ant lion rapidly digs itself into sand, and as the loose material caves in on it, it tosses it out with sharp jerky motions of its head. Most ants stumbling into the pit quickly lose their foothold in the sliding sand of its slope and are easily captured. Those that succeed in temporarily avoiding the deadly jaws are bombarded with repeated sprays of sand until they, too, come tumbling down and can be seized by the ant lion. It sucks their bodies dry, and hurls the empty carcasses out of the pit. As this photograph shows, they lie around littering the rim of the trap, testifying to its deadly efficiency.

57. The work of carpenter ants (*Camponotus herculeanus*). These ants carve their nests in the heart wood of timber, sometimes weakening man-made structures to the point of collapse, although they are not nearly as destructive as termites. Their intricately chambered galleries, resembling abstract modern sculpture in design, are constructed as though the ants understood the structural properties of wood, which they hollow out in a way designed to weaken it least.

58. Inside view of the nest of the bald-faced hornet (*Vespula maculata*) showing the tiers of horizontal combs together with a cross-section of the encasing walls. These walls consist of many layers of a paper-like substance separated by air spaces for equally efficient insulation against both heat and cold. Scientific measurements have established that the insulating power of this structure, which was only 1³/₄ inches thick, is equivalent to that of a 16-inch brick wall. But whereas one cubic inch of brick masonry weighs 27.1 grams, the equivalent volume of this hornets nest's wall material weighs only 0.2 grams.

59. *Top row:* With the coming of spring, the wasp queens that survived the winter start building their nests. This row of pictures shows a common paper wasp (*Polistes*) at work on the open comb in the cells of which it is going to lay its eggs. The forthcoming larvae will develop into sterile workers whose job it will be to enlarge the comb further and to feed and generally take care of the following generations of wasps.

Bottom: Close-up of a large *Polistes* nest in summer. Unlike the hornets, the paper wasps do not enclose their combs with protective envelopes but leave them exposed, although they usually select a sheltered nesting site. The open cells contain eggs or larvae, the capped cells pupae.

60. A row of nests of the mud dauber wasp (*Trypoxylon politum*). Each ridge in the herring-bone pattern of these "organ pipes" represents a tiny ball of soft mud which the wasp gathered near the edge of a puddle and transported to the nesting site, where it carefully patted it into place, instinctively guided by "rules" which are as strict as those followed by a master mason. The tubes are subdivided into a number of individual cells, each of which contains an egg, together with a supply of live yet paralyzed spiders which the wasp had captured and deposited there as food for the larva. After pupation, the mature insect breaks through the wall of the tube and flies away, leaving the "organ pipes" riddled with holes, as shown in this photograph.

61. *Top:* Entrance to the burrow of a ground-nesting solitary bee.

Bottom: I found large numbers of these little mounds capping small holes in the ground along an abandoned road near Montauk Point on Long Island, New York. But none of the experts whom I consulted was able to tell me by what kind of insect they had been made.

62—63. Patterns made by the larvae of different kinds of bark beetles. After drilling through the bark, these beetles carve a straight or curved tunnel in the inner bark or at the juncture of the bark and sapwood. Along this gallery the female deposits her eggs in an arrangement that is often different from one species to another. When the eggs hatch, the larvae fan out more or less at right angles to the axis of the tunnel, each larva digging in hungrily and making its own little tunnel which gradually increases in diameter as the larva grows, feeding on the soft layers of cambium and phloem. Since a tree's life depends upon these two vital, paper-thin layers which alone enable it to form new wood and conduct nutrients and water between leaves and roots, the havoc which bark beetles raise can be considerable and may even cause the death of the affected tree.

64. These circular, precision-drilled holes are the work of mollusks known as "shipworms" (*Teredo navalis*), a type of greatly elongated clam which grows as much as twenty-four inches long, although its rudimentary shell consists only of two small half-inch valves, which these animals use as boring tools. Shipworms, which spend their entire adult life inside submerged timber, can do enormous damage to untreated wood of wharf pilings and the hulls of ships, which they riddle with their tunnels until the structure disintegrates.

65. Other creatures besides spiders can produce silk. Shown here is the communal web of the North American fall webworm (*Hyphantria*), a relative of the tent caterpillar (*Malacosoma*) which spins its nest in spring. Although it appears flimsy and loosely woven, this house of silk is strong enough to protect its inhabitants from caterpillar-eating birds and tight enough to keep out the rain.

◀ 54
55 ▶

◀62
63▶

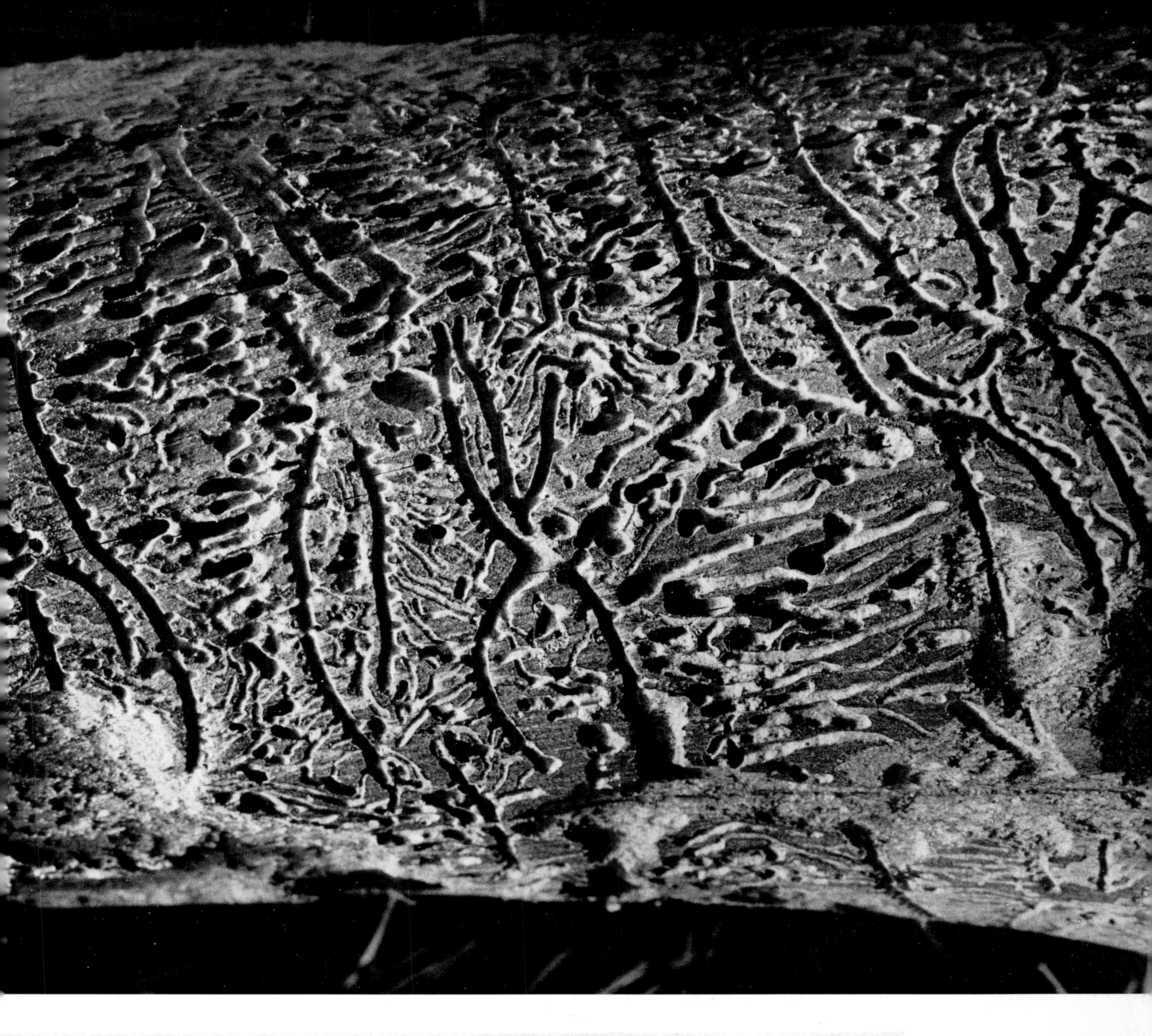

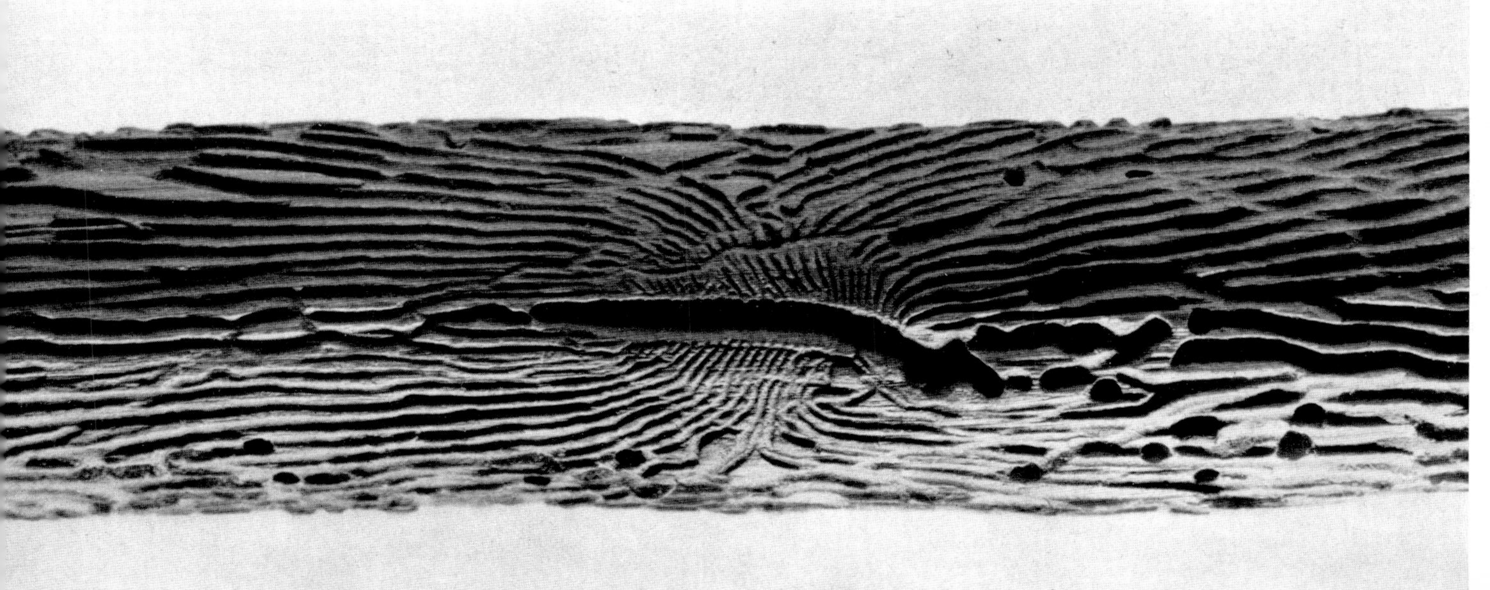

VI

Spider Webs

Among the many fascinating works of animals, none are structurally more interesting or aesthetically more satisfying than the big wheel-like webs of the orb-weaving spiders. And never do these webs appear more beautiful than at sunrise on a chilly morning in fall, when thousands of pearly dew drops adorn their strands and cascades of shimmering light reveal their full exquisite workmanship and further enhance their charm. Then they seem like necklaces of liquid diamonds magically scattered among the weeds.

Spider silk is a fabulous material of many qualities which surpasses structural steel in tensile strength. It is secreted by special glands, extruded in liquid form through the finger-like spinnerets located at the tip of the spider's abdomen, and, when stretched, hardens into dry lines. Spiders produce different kinds of silk for different purposes, and the spider has complete control over its spinnerets. Depending upon the occasion, it can produce silk that is coarse, tough, and dry (for the radial strands of an orb web, which must be nonsticky because they provide the scaffold on which the spider walks); sticky and elastic (this kind of thread is used for the spiral of the orb web, which ensnares the spider's prey and must be able to withstand its struggles); thin and strong (to be used as a life-line by the spider in case of an emergency drop from its web); and downy-fluffy (to serve as swaddling material for the spider's eggs).

Not all species of spiders make webs, but of those that do, each works according to its own distinctive design. These designs can be classified into four main groups: more or less circular and radial-symmetrical webs suspended in the vertical plane like the web of the garden spider (plate 66); webs with supporting strands extending in all directions like the web of the doily spider (plate 73); webs constructed in the shape of a funnel expanding from some natural hole or crevice like the web of the grass spider (plate 69); and tubular webs that line the walls of a hole dug by the spider itself like the web of the trapdoor spider (plate 95).

66. This is the web of a type of garden spider, the banded argiope (*Argiope trifasciata*). At its focal point, the weaver herself waits for the web to dry so that the daily business of catching insects can begin. Like all orb weavers, she sits with her head facing down, presumably so that in an emergency she can instantly drop to the ground at the end of her silken life-line. This web was photographed early in the morning on a grassy slope in Connecticut.

67. Close-up of the central portion of another garden spider's web; it clearly shows the dew-covered threads of silk. This silk is so fine that it is virtually invisible, as evident from the threads near the center of the web that are free of dew.

68. Orb weaver webs decorating the ironwork of a bridge across the Housatonic River in Connecticut. The web shown at the top, left, is unfinished, probably because some mishap befell the spider before it could complete its work—the sticky spiral is always put in last. All webs were photographed shortly after sunrise before the dew had time to evaporate. Later, when dry, these webs are all but invisible because their threads are so fine.

69. The funnel-web of a grass spider (*Agelenopsis pennsylvanica*). This type of web is common in the stone walls that border the fields in New England. Normally, the owner waits in the protective darkness of its silk-lined tunnel for insects to become enmeshed in the sheet-web that is so invitingly spread out in front of its lair. But by gently shaking this web with a grass stalk I was able to coax the spider to leave its hole and pose.

70—71. The web of a grass spider (*Agelenopsis*). On cool mornings in fall, large numbers of these sheet-webs can often be seen decorating the lawns of New England, where they look like so many silk handkerchiefs spread out to dry. But as soon as the dew which made them visible has evaporated and they are dry, they seem to disappear as mysteriously as they came. This picture clearly shows how skillfully these spiders suspend their silken sheets from individual blades of grass, making these structures look like miniature circus tents.

72. *Top:* The hackle-banded web of a Florida spider (*Filistata hibernalis*) photographed in the corner of a woodshed where this sheet-web fanned out from a crack between two boards in which the spider had its funnel-like retreat.

Bottom: The funnel-and-sheet web of a grass spider (*Agelenopsis*), dew-sprinkled, lightly rests on the top leaves of small plants.

73. The two-storied web of the bowl-and-doily spider (*Frontinella communis*), photographed in Connecticut. Guy lines attached to strategic points and hauled taut ensure that this structure keeps its parabolic shape.

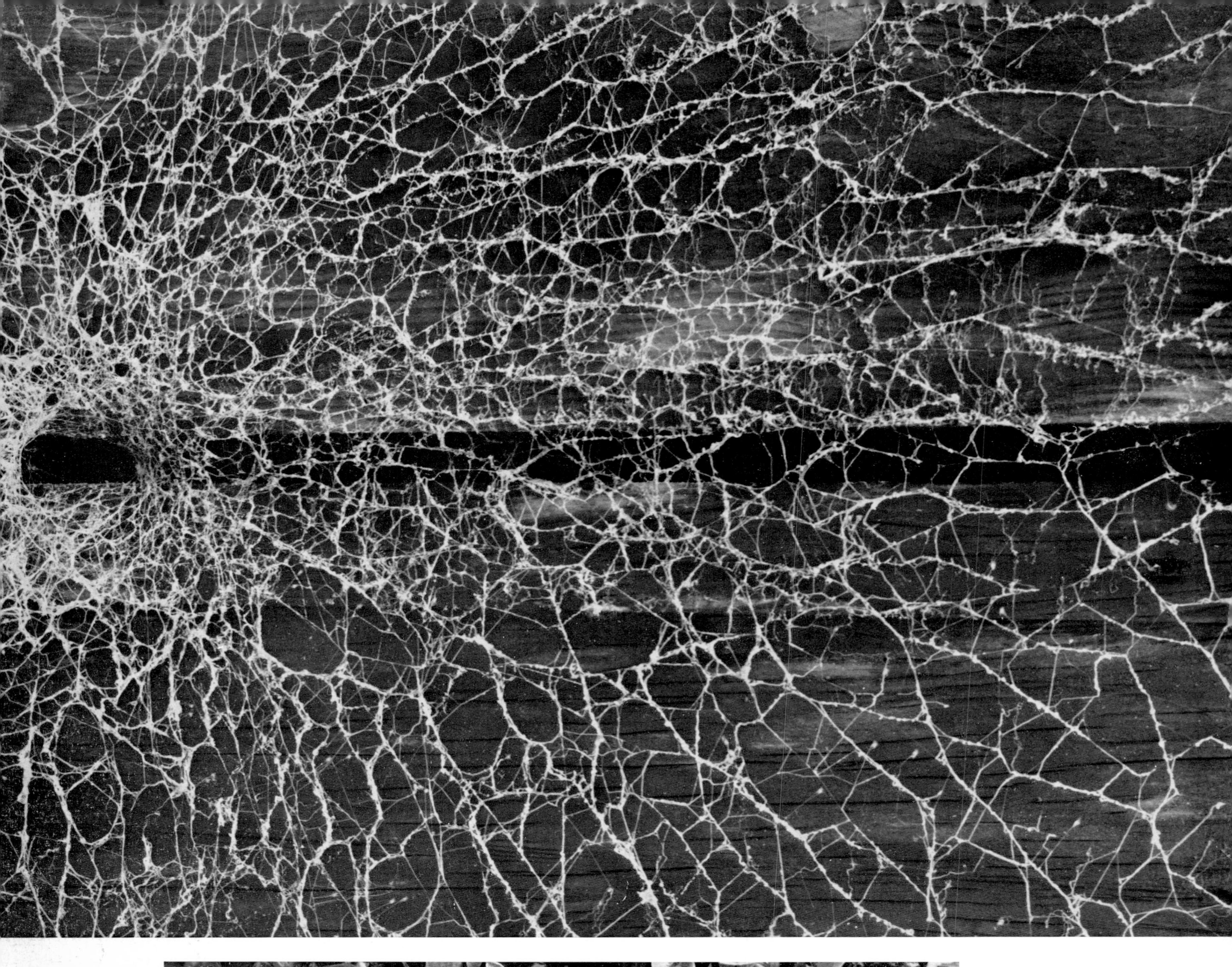

VII

A Close Look at Spiders

Most people have an instinctive aversion to spiders which may even approach the intensity of a phobia—an uncontrollable terror which seems all the more unreasonable as, except for a few species, notably the black widows (plate 88), no North American spider is potentially dangerous to man. Although the bite of every spider is poisonous, this poison is for killing insects, not people, and, according to the best authorities, even the bite of the largest and most ferocious-looking tarantula (plate 84) is no more dangerous or painful than a bee sting. On the contrary, it would be much more logical to protect spiders because they are highly beneficial to man, since they kill an enormous number of insects, the majority of which must be classified as "pests."

Personally, I find spiders extraordinarily interesting and, looked at closely, even beautiful in a weird and barbaric way. Their webs and traps alone should provide an endless source of fascinating study to those who are interested in the relationship between adaptation to specific conditions, purpose, structure, and form. And the infinite variety of their colors and shapes should be a delight to any unbiased person able to appreciate strange and unfamiliar sights. So great is this variety that the only characteristics common to all spiders are that their bodies consist of two main parts, the cephalothorax and the abdomen (the bodies of insects consist of three parts: head, thorax, and abdomen); that they have four pairs of legs (insects have three); and that they have only simple eyes (usually eight, but there are exceptions), whereas insects have both simple and compound eyes.

It would please me if the following pictures would prove to be provocative enough to induce the reader to overcome whatever prejudices against spiders he may have and to take a new look at these fascinating creatures—to see the interesting in the alien, and the beautiful in the bizarre. Magnified many times their natural size so that even fine detail becomes effective, spiders resemble some of the monsters with which writers of science-fiction like to populate "Planet X"; but these grotesque and even frightening creatures are not products of fantasy but living testimony to the endless wealth of form and types of behavior which adaptation to specific conditions has produced here on earth.

74. A female wolf spider (*Geolycosa patellonigra*) and her brood. Immediately upon hatching, the spiderlings climb on their mother's back, where, like a living fur coat two and three layers deep, they remain for some time before they finally disperse. They start eating only after their second molt and subsist until then by digesting the remainders of the embryonic yolk which remained in their midgut. The adult spider's eight eyes are clearly visible in this photograph.

75. *Top and center:* A female wolf spider (*Lycosa aspersa*) with her egg sack. Before she lays her eggs, the female looks for a sheltered, flat spot of ground, where she spins a coarse mat of silk. On this she weaves a second, slightly bowl-shaped disk of fluffy white silk, in the center of which she deposits her eggs. This done, she covers the eggs with a separate sheet of downy silk, then detaches the disk from its supporting mat and folds it over its content, tucking in the corners and shaping the whole structure until it forms a sphere the size of a large pea. This sphere the spider ties to her spinnerets and carries around wherever she goes until the eggs hatch and the spiderlings emerge and climb onto her back. The empty egg sack is then discarded.

Bottom: A female wolf spider (*Lycosa* [*Trochosa*] *avara*) carrying her young on her back. One spiderling has fallen off, but will soon scramble back again and resume its ride. Its actual size can be gauged by comparing it with the grains of sand—

◀ 74

the magnification of this photograph is about ten times linear.

76. *Top row:* Egg sacks of the garden spider (*Argiope aurantia*). Each sack is about the size of a fiftycent piece and contains from one hundred to two hundred eggs. Strands of silk like guy wire form an elastic suspension system which protects the eggs from rough jolts when the supporting weed or branch is buffeted by the wind.

Bottom: Spiderlings emerging from the egg sack, their beady eyes contrasting startlingly with their pallid, semitransparent forms. The two fingers at the right, which hold the egg sack, establish the scale of the picture.

77. Baby orb weavers (*Argiope aurantia*) leaving their egg sack descend on silken threads to the ground.

78—79. A large Florida wolf spider (*Lycosa ammophila*) prowling the grass-root jungle. Wolf spiders do not spin webs but hunt their prey on foot. This one belongs to a particularly beautiful species distinguished by a mauve or rose-colored fur coat effectively set off with dark brown markings.

80. A Florida trapdoor spider (*Cyclocosmia truncata*) at the end of its underground burrow, which the abdomen of this species fits as a cork fits a bottle. Stiff bristles around its perimeter ensure a tight seal and, in conjunction with the hard and flat surface, make it virtually impossible for a predator to dislodge this spider from its underground retreat.

80—81. *Cyclocosmia truncata* seen from the rear. Its tail-plate, with its facelike design, brings to mind symbolic Aztec representations of the sun. The eyelike spots are not eyes however, but, like the pseudo-eye designs found in so many moths, caterpillars, and other insects, may have survival value by frightening off potential enemies.

82. A garden spider (*Argiope aurantia*). Like all orb weavers, it rests head down in its web. The white patch is called a *stabilimentum* and is typical of this species (other species make *stabilimenta* of different designs). Its exact purpose is unknown, but by showing up so clearly it may induce flying insects to veer around it only to be caught in the almost invisible sticky outside strands of the web.

83. A Florida spider (*Uloborus geniculatus*) patiently waits head down in a web so fine that it is virtually invisible.

84. A tarantula (*Dugesiella sp.*) from the arid Southwest. This is the largest North American spider, more frightening-looking than dangerous because its bite, although mildly poisonous, hurts no more than a bee sting and does just as little permanent damage to man.

85. A long-legged cellar spider (*Pholcus phalangioides*). In contrast to the massive tarantula, this spider looks positively ethereal, its eight sensitive legs delicately probing the air and informing the spider about its surroundings.

86. Looking baleful, its poison fangs sunk deep into its victim's chest, a wolf spider (*Geolycosa patellonigra*) is draining a grasshopper of its juices. Spiders play an important role in maintaining a balance in nature. Without their active participation, insect damage to plants and crops would assume enormous proportions. On the other hand, birds and many species of wasps (such as the mud daubers whose nest is shown in plate 60), by catching spiders as food for their larvae, keep the spider population from becoming disproportionate. Nature, if unhampered by man, always achieves a balance among its components, each of its creatures finding its share, the welfare of one depending directly or indirectly upon the welfare of all others.

87. With its eight headlight-like eyes, seen under thirty times linear magnification, this fisher spider

(*Dolomedes sp.*) seems a formidable creature indeed. Actually, it is not only harmless, but beneficial to man, its bite rarely worse than that of a mosquito.

88. Looking at you with a beady eye, this is the famous black widow (*Latrodectus mactans*), almost the only American spider potentially dangerous to man. Although more common in the South, black widows occur in every state in the Union except Alaska. They prefer dark locations and are commonly found in woodsheds and places where flies congregate, such as refuse dumps and outhouses, where they like to spin their scraggly webs directly beneath the seat. The black widow is a relatively small spider, easily identified by its shiny blackberry-like abdomen marked on the underside with the famous red hourglass design. Although its bite is usually extremely painful and recovery from it may take up to two weeks and necessitate hospitalization, it is rarely fatal. Of 380 documented cases of black-widow bites, only seventeen resulted in death.

89. This is a close-up of a daddy longlegs (*Leiobunum sp.*), in this case an invalid who had lost three of its eight legs yet got around remarkably well on the remaining five. Structurally, it is a fascinating creature—its legs attached to its body by ball-and-socket joints that freely swivel in all directions, its eyes ensconced periscope-like in a little "turret" atop its tanklike body—a harmless scavenger bumping and swaying erratically along on its suspension-legs in search of rotting animal and vegetable matter on which it feeds.

◀ 76
77 ▶

◀ 80
81 ▶
◀ 78/79

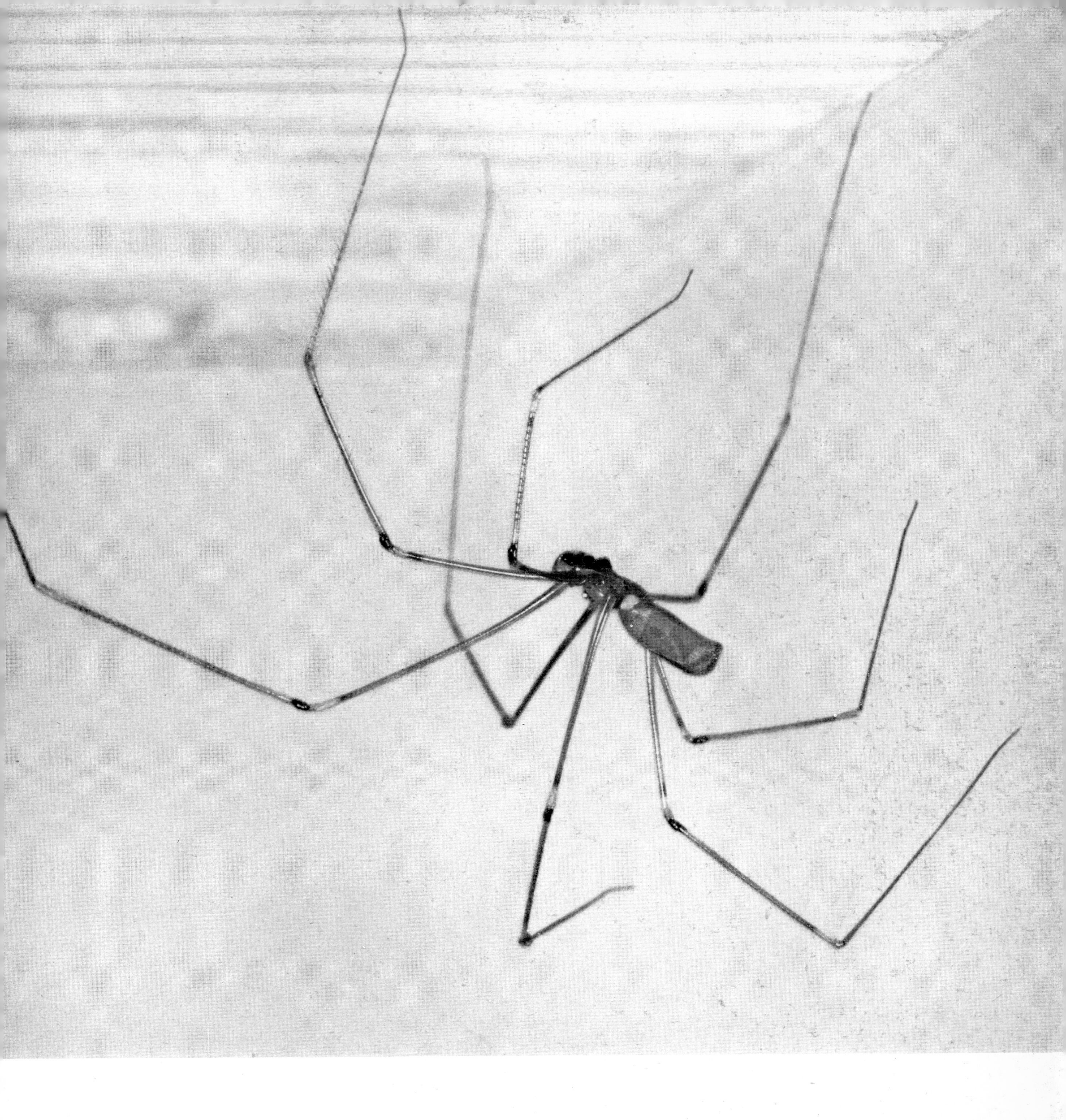

◀ 84
85 ▶

◀ 86
87 ▶

VIII

Animal Camouflage

Outward appearances are often deceptive. This is particularly true in regard to many animals—especially those of the so-called "lower orders"—whose coloration and often also structure and form have no resemblance to what one commonly expects an animal to look like: insects that look like twigs, leaves, or bark; birds which, when resting on the ground, blend marvelously with their surroundings of dead leaves dappled by light and shadow; birds' eggs that perfectly match the pebbles among which the female customarily makes her nest; protective cocoons that look like parts of the plant which furnished the material of which they are made; fish that look like seaweed or the ground on which they commonly rest.

These and other resemblances to ordinary inanimate or inedible matter have, of course, a great survival value to the respective species of animals, whose members are more often overlooked by predators than less well camouflaged types. And the more perfect the camouflage, the greater the likelihood that the individual thus protected will survive and reproduce its kind—a fact which Darwin was one of the first to recognize and which plays an important part in his theory of evolution.

The classic example of animal camouflage is the Asiatic dead-leaf butterfly (*Kallima*) which, when resting with its wings folded, resembles a dead leaf to an almost unbelievable degree, down to the last detail of venation, not to forget a "stalk" formed by projections of the hind wings. Other amazingly effective examples of animal camouflage are found among the mantises, some of which look more leaflike than real leaves, particularly the Australian walking leaf (*Phyllium siccifolium*) and the Asiatic mantis (*Gongylus trachelophyllus*); and among the fishes, where the South American leaf fish (*Monocirrhus polyacanthus*), the Mediterranean pipe fishes (*Nerophis* and *Syngnathus*), the Pacific sea dragon (*Phycodurus eques*) and the Atlantic frog fish (*Histrio histrio*) furnish outstanding examples of animal camouflage.

All camouflage is founded on three principles: the apparent break-up of familiar forms based upon "optical illusions;" the suppression of the shadow effect; and the match in coloration (and often also form) between the animal and objects of its surroundings.

For example, under natural conditions, strong surface patterns consisting of stripes or spots seem to "break up" the actual form of an animal and make it blend with its surroundings much more effectively than if the animal had been uniformly colored and thus presented a clear-cut outline against its background. However, exceptional conditions produce exceptions to this rule, such as the uniformly white protective coloration of some animals in winter or of those that live in polar regions. There, "solid" white blends more perfectly with the white of the snow than a "pattern," which would make the animal stand out conspicuously. Animals that show this concealing effect (somatolysis) particularly well are many insects, toads and frogs, snakes, spotted and striped members of the cat family, and many ground-nesting birds.

All animals have volume, and all bodies with volume cast shadows. As a result, despite the most perfect camouflage, an animal may stand out conspicuously if its shadow forms a sharp black outline which reveals its form to the roving eye of a predator. Hence, effective camouflage demands that this shadow effect be suppressed as much as possible. This can be accomplished in several ways: the resting animal may assume a crouching position which brings its body into close contact with the ground or other support on which it rests, so that no shadow can form beneath it; this is typical of many young birds, reptiles, and resting moths. Or, the animal has evolved a flattened body or special flanges or flaps which in resting position make contact with its support and thus inhibit the formation

◀ 90

of shadows; this is commonly found among certain types of insects, reptiles, and fish. And finally, there is "counter-shading" (Thayer's principle) which manifests itself in a color scheme according to which the animal's back is darker than its underside so that the two effects, top-lighted dark back and shaded light-colored underside, more or less match each other and harsh shadows are avoided. This form of camouflage is most often found in small vertebrates and birds and in very many fishes, whose backs are slate-colored, brown, or dark blue and whose undersides are light gray or silvery white.

The last form of camouflage—match in coloration and form between an animal and specific objects of its surroundings—has reached an almost unbelievable degree of perfection in many insects and their larval form. Seen against a neutral background in sharp illumination, a bird, for example, will always look like a bird and a mammal like a mammal. But even under these brutally revealing conditions many insects do not look like insects at all but like twigs, leaves, or inocuous bits of bark. The best-known representatives of this group are probably the stick insects (walking stick, *Diapheromera femorata*) and the inch-worms or measuring-worms, the caterpillars of the geometrid moths.

To find outstanding examples of animal camouflage, one does not have to go to distant parts of the world. All the following photographs show common species of animals which can be found almost anywhere in the United States by anyone who takes the trouble to look for them. Although perhaps not quite as spectacular as some of their exotic equivalents, they nevertheless prove to what an extraordinary degree evolution and adaptation can change the color, structure, and form of animal—convincing proof of the survival value of camouflage.

90. Toad fish (*Opsanus tau*). Photographed in only inches of water in a tidepool near Westport, Connecticut, where it was trapped by the receding tide, this fish is virtually invisible due to camouflage: break-up of form through banded patterns, coloration that matches the bottom of the pool, and close contact with the ground as a result of a flattened body and membranous appendages held low which keep revealing shadows to a minimum.

91. These objects that look like parts of plants or trees are the protective casings of "bagworms"—the collective popular name of the larvae of the moth family Psychidae. Each species builds its own characteristic little "home" from bits of twigs and leaves cemented to the outside of an inner sleeve spun of silk in which the caterpillar spends its entire life until the moment of transformation into the adult moth. If the moth is a male, it leaves its "bag" and flies away in search of females. But if it is a female, it often never leaves its home except, perhaps, to mate with a male, after which it crawls back into its "bag," where it lays its eggs and dies, leaving its carcass, pupal case, and last larval skin, together with the egg mass, in the "bag."

92. An owlet moth (family Noctuidae) passing the day in sleep. The color and pattern of its front wings not only match those of the bark but even imitate the kind of lichen that usually grows on the trees which this moth habitually and instinctively chooses as resting places during the day. However, the hind wings of many owlet moths are brightly colored in red, orange, yellow, or blue, set off with bold bands of black. This "flash-coloration" probably has survival value: a predator pursuing such a moth may focus its attention on these brightly "flashing" colors, only to be utterly thrown off the track when they suddenly disappear as the moth plasters itself against the trunk of a tree and in its typical resting position hides its colors beneath its front wings.

93. Caterpillar of a prominent moth (*Notodonta*) distinguished by a cryptic pattern, coloration, and shape that make it extremely difficult to spot in its natural habitat. However, other species of prominent moths exist whose larvae display bright "warning colors" (the aposematic effect) instead

of cryptic coloration; these larvae are able to secrete a powerful acid, which some species can even squirt to distances of several inches when attacked. Here we have the opposite of camouflage—clear warning to predators that they had better leave these caterpillars alone.

94—95. Not all spiders catch their prey in webs. The trapdoor spiders, for example, make silk-lined tubes in the soil, flitted with silk-hinged trapdoors which they camouflage to blend perfectly with the surrounding ground (in this case, the moss-covered bank of a drainage ditch in Florida). Peeking out from beneath the partly raised door, the spider patiently waits for things to happen. When a suitable victim approaches within striking distance, the spider pounces.

These two photographs show the identical area. The gaping hole is the entrance to the lair of the trapdoor spider, *Ummidia audouini,* the trapdoor of which the photographer has propped open with a stick. How innocuous this deadly trap appears when closed is shown in the opposite picture.

96. A katydid (family Tettigoniidae) which in color and form (its body is strongly compressed laterally) imitates a leaf. Katydids are tireless musicians which, during a summer, may produce their well-known song up to fifty million times.

97. An ambush bug *(Phymata erosa)* sucking dry a hover fly which it has caught. Its yellow and brown coloration in conjunction with an irregular knobby form make this bug look like some dried part of the plant—usually goldenrod—where this killer hides within a cluster of flowers, waiting patiently for any insect that might be unfortunate enough to come within its reach.

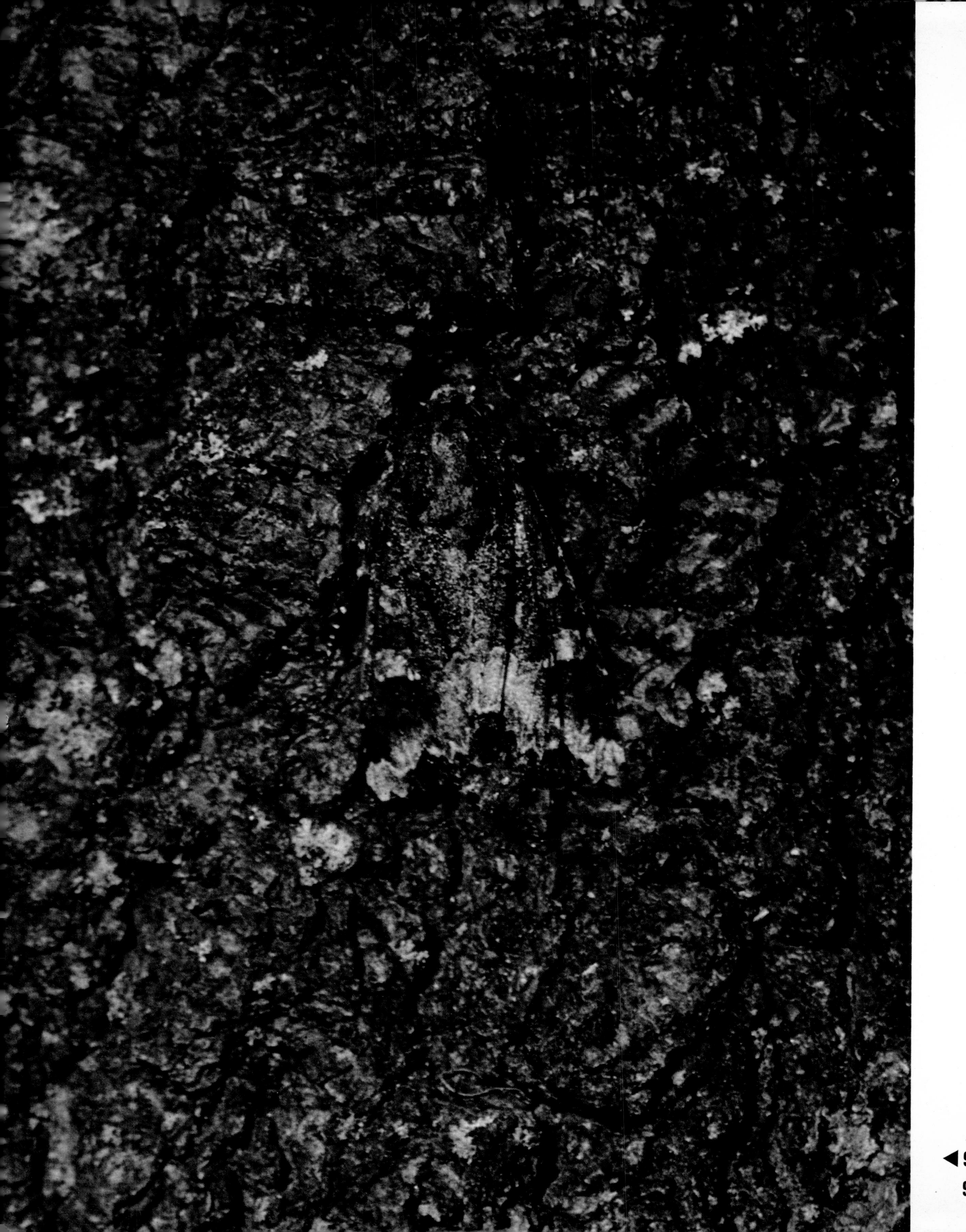

◀92

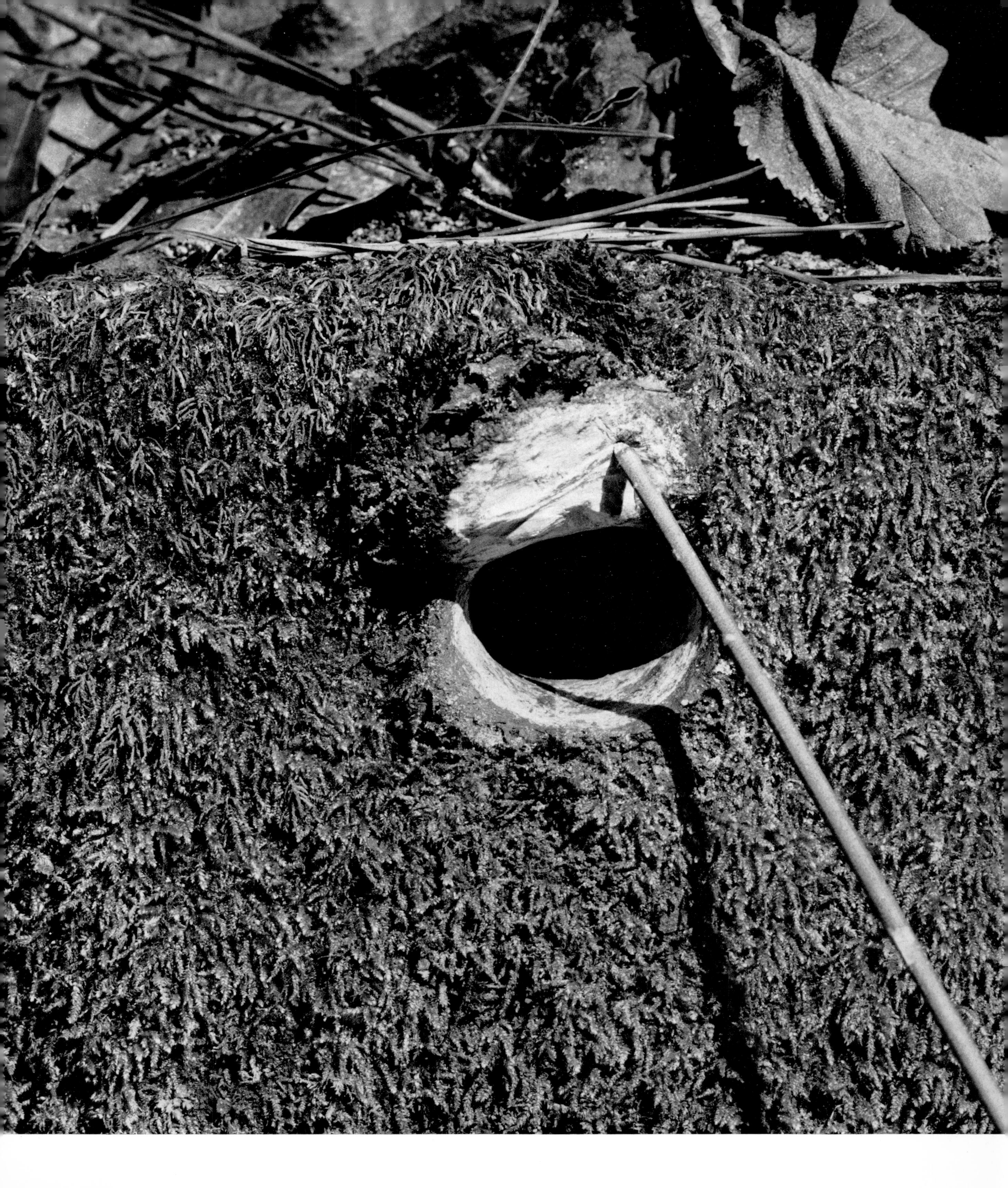

IX

Insect Close-ups

Most people can distinguish a butterfly from a beetle and a bedbug from a bee, but very few know what these creatures look like when, so to speak, they are seen face to face. Yet the faces of insects are as interesting and variegated as are their general forms, as the following photographs will prove.

But first: how does one distinguish an insect from other kinds of "bugs," such as, for instance, spiders, centipedes, millipedes, mites, sowbugs, scorpions, lobsters, crabs—all of which are members of the same phylum (the so-called jointed-legged animals or Arthropoda) although they are not insects (which form a special "class" within the phylum Arthropoda)? This is not difficult because only insects have the following basic characteristics: their bodies consist of three main parts: head, thorax (middle section), and abdomen (rear section); they have three pairs of legs, which are attached to the thorax and, usually, they also have wings; and they possess only one pair of antennae. Spiders, for example, have only two main body parts, four pairs of legs, and no wings and no antennae; millipedes have a very large number of legs (but never a thousand; two hundred is about the maximum) arranged in double pairs, whereas centipedes have a lesser number of legs arranged in single pairs, and their front legs are modified into hollow clawlike pincers suitable for injecting venom into their prey; lobsters and crabs have two main body parts, many pairs of legs, and two pairs of antennae; and so forth.

Insects are the largest and most successful class of animals in the world, comprising an estimated seven hundred thousand species of the million or so decribed and named species of animals. Many species have yet to be discovered. They have penetrated into virtually every region of the globe except the oceans. Specially adapted types of insects are found in the bleak waste lands of the arctic and antarctic; others live in eternal darkness in deep underground caves; still others have been found in the Himalayas at altitudes up to twenty thousand feet. Some species have even adapted to such extraordinary environments as hot springs, where they thrive in water of 120 degrees Fahrenheit. The larvae of the brine-fly live in evaporated lakes containing a concentrated saline solution, while the larvae of the petroleum fly have made the pools of crude oil in the southern California oilfields their home.

In their development from birth to death, the overwhelming majority of insects go through a series of different stages. The females of these insects lay eggs from which hatch larvae that look entirely different from the adults—the caterpillar of the butterfly, the grub of the beetle, the maggot of the fly. In due time, the larvae enter a dormant stage—the pupa—during which the transformation into the adult insect occurs. Finally, the transformation completed, the adult insect breaks its pupal shell, crawls out, expands and hardens its wings, and goes about its business of living and propagation.

Although some 87 per cent of all insects go through these four stages (that is, have complete metamorphosis) about 12 per cent undergo gradual metamorphosis instead. These insects, of which the dragonflies, grasshoppers, and true bugs are well-known representatives, have immature stages that appear rather similar to the adults but lack wings. Called nymphs, they develop gradually via a series of molts into the adult form (they undergo indirect or incomplete metamorphosis). And finally, there are a very few, very primitive insects in which there is virtually no difference between the immature stages and the adults except in size and the fact that the adults are sexually active and the larvae are not. Such insects do not undergo metamorphosis but their numbers comprise less than one per cent of the entire insect population.

Insect eggs are very small, inconspicuous, and extremely well protected, sometimes tough-shelled capsules within which the embryo can safely de-

◀ 98

velop. Larvae and nymphs merely eat, digest, grow, and store food reserves for the later transformation into the imago—the adult insect; their sexual organs are not yet formed and they are therefore incapable of reproduction. The pupa, found only in insects with complete metamorphosis, is a vessel which, outwardly seemingly dormant, nevertheless is internally seething with activity, for it is during this stage that the entire body of the insect is reconstructed and transformed from the larval form into the adult. And finally there is the imago,—whose main purpose in life—often to such a degree that it does not even eat at all but survives only on the food reserves stored during its larval stage—is to find a mate and reproduce its kind.

All insects belong to the class Hexapoda (which means six-footed), a division of the phylum Arthropoda. But although, scientifically speaking, all "bugs" are insects, not all insects are "bugs." For the insects again are divided into a number of different "orders," of which the true bugs (Hemiptera) comprise only one (typical representatives are the bedbug, the stink bug, and the ambush bug shown in plate 97). Other orders are the Lepidoptera—the butterflies and moths (plates 92, 93, 102, 103, 113); the Coleoptera—the beetles (plates 98, 112); the Orthoptera, to which the grasshoppers, crickets, katydids, cockroaches, mantises, and walking sticks belong (plates 96, 99, 104, 105); the Diptera or true flies (plates 100, 101, 106, 107); the Hymenoptera—the bees, wasps, ants, and sawflies (plates 110, 111); the Ephemeroptera—the mayflies (plate 108); the Mecoptera—the scorpion flies (plate 109); and a number of other orders whose members are popularly less well known.

Insects have perhaps a greater influence upon man's life than any other class of animals. Many deadly diseases, such as yellow fever, cholera, malaria, sleeping sickness, and typhoid fever, as well as some thirty less common types, are transmitted by insects, especially mosquitoes, flies, and fleas. Other insects can do enormous damage to plants intended for human use, the best known example being the gigantic swarms of locusts, which leave desolation and famine in their wake. There is, however, a very important positive side to the role which insects play as far as man is concerned: many of our most cherished plants and trees depend entirely upon insects for their pollination and would quickly become extinct if these insects were destroyed. And many species of insects are highly beneficial to man because they feed upon harmful insects, which they destroy in enormous quantities; among these beneficial insects are the predatory wasps and mantises, the robber flies which prey on a wide variety of insects and spiders; the dragonflies, one of whose favorite foods is mosquitoes; and the lace-wings and ladybird beetles, which consume enormous amounts of aphids. As a matter of fact, despite man's ingenious poison sprays with which he tries to keep the insect population within tolerable bounds, the main factor which prevents insects from completely getting out of control and overwhelming the rest of the world are other insects—another example of what is popularly known as "keeping the balance in nature."

98. This is not the head of a placid calf but that of a long-horned beetle (family Cerambycidae), magnified here some thirty times linear. These beetles are characterized by relatively slender bodies which in size range from less than a quarter of an inch to fully six inches in length, and by exceptionally long antennae. Their wood-boring grubs can do a great deal of damage to trees.

99. Head of a cricket (family Gryllidae), enlarged here some twenty times linear. Because of its highly polished, deep black surface which reproduces either as a brilliant highlight or dead black, it is extremely difficult to photograph. The ball-and-socket joints of the two antennae and the two compound eyes are clearly visible.

100. Head of a tachina fly (familiy Tachinidae). This is a member of a family of insects that is highly beneficial to man. Their larvae live within the bodies of other insects, many of which belong to

the most destructive and harmful species, feeding on their tissues and in the process killing them. In fact, the economic value of the tachina flies is so great that some species are reared in captivity in large numbers, to be released in regions outside their home territory in an effort to cope with sudden outbreaks of insect infestations. On such occasions, they have often proved more successful in combatting the pests than poisonous insecticides with their always undesirable and often dangerous side effects.

101. Head of a horsefly (*family Tabanidae*). The members of this family are noted and feared because of the bloodsucking habits of the females; also, in the western United States, horseflies have been found to transmit tularemia (rabbit fever), an often fatal disease. The compound eyes of most horseflies are breathtakingly beautiful structures characterized by stripes, patches, and bands of brilliant, iridescent color. These colors are caused not by pigments but by prismatic structures within the integument which break up the white light into its spectral colors. Unfortunately for collectors these structures dry up and shrink and the magic colors disappear when the fly dies.

102. Head and front part of a monarch butterfly (*Anosia plexippus*). This conspicuously colored butterfly is one of our largest and most beautiful insects, whose highly unpleasant taste (its caterpillars feed on the mildly poisonous milkweed) gives it a high degree of immunity from birds. Its coloration seems to be a typical example of "warning color" (aposematic coloration), since the viceroy butterfly (*Limenitis archippus*), an apparently "tasty" insect, mimicks the monarch and resembles it so closely that it also enjoys relative immunity from birds, who apparently mistake it for a monarch.

103. Head of the common clothes moth (*Tineola bisselliella*), a member of the "microlepidoptera" group who rarely exceed half an inch in size. They are scavengers whose larvae live mainly on wool, mohair, fur, etc., and can become very destructive. This photograph shows the front part of the moth, its left compound eye clearly visible, in about sixty times natural size.

104. Head of a katydid (family Tettigoniidae). Because of its cryptic coloration (*see Plate* 96 and accompanying caption) it is rarely seen, but anyone who has ever spent a summer evening in the New England countryside knows its lovely, although at times irritating, call.

105. Head of a grasshopper (family Locustidae). It is to this family that the famous swarming locusts belong, one or more species of which are found on each major continent.

106. Head of a male horsefly (family Tabanidae). These insects are characterized by their enormous compound eyes, which, particularly in the males, cover the larger part of the head. They consist of thousands of minute, individual eyes, each a six-sided facet containing its own tiny lens and retina pointing in a different direction. Together (although they cannot be focused), they combine to produce a complete picture of the insect's surroundings. Although we have, of course, no means of ascertaining the exact nature of the image produced within the insect's brain, experiments seem to prove that, although vision seems sharp only at relatively short distances, motion is very keenly perceived, probably because an object in motion stimulates one facet after another as it passes across the insect's field of vision. And motion detection is, of course, of the greatest survival value to the insect, since a moving object signifies usually either an enemy or a potential meal.

107. Head of a robber fly (family Asilidae). Robber flies are powerful predators which prey on other insects by capturing them on the wing or by pouncing on them from the air. Their long, bristle-covered legs are especially adapted to hold their victims securely; the fly then punctures them with its short, strong beak and sucks dry.

108. Head of a mayfly (order Ephemeroptera). Mayflies are best known for their ephemeral adult lives, which often last only for a few hours, and the astronomical numbers in which they sometimes emerge on warm summer evenings—spattering and clogging the windshields of automobiles and, in lake-front and riverside communities, posing major problems to the sanitation department crews who have to clean up the streets the morning after the mayflies' nuptial flights. The only purpose of the adult mayfly is to mate and produce eggs. Accordingly, their legs are weak and their wings delicate, since their work is usually done in a few hours; mouth parts are degenerate or lacking entirely; the digestive system is merely filled with air instead of food to make the insect more buoyant and reduce its specific gravity; and in many species, the bodies of the females are stuffed with eggs from one end to the other all the way up into the head.

109. Head of a scorpion fly (family Panorpidae). These harmless and mildly beneficial insects are characterized by a curiously elongated head which is not a sucking beak but ends in tiny jaws used only to feed on dead or injured insects, fruit juices, and sap.

110. Head of an ant (family Formicidae). Together with the bees, the ants are structurally among the most advanced and specialized, socially the most highly organized, and generally the most interesting of all insects. However, since a complete discussion of the characteristics and accomplishments of ants would fill volumes, only a few of the most fascinating aspects can be mentioned here.

The longevity of ants is greater than that of most other insects, and records exist of ant queens that lived for twenty years and workers that lived five years and more. And since ants are capable not only of learning from experience, but also of remembering and even, in some not yet fully understood ways, of passing on their knowledge to younger generations of ants, it is no wonder that their societies are often incredibly complex, highly organized and diversified, and utterly efficient in their struggle for existence.

Some ants practice slavery and raid the nests of other ant communities (of a different species), killing the workers, carrying off the larvae and pupae, and taking them home, where they complete their metamorphosis to assume their new functions. One species, the amazon ant, is in fact so dependent on "slaves" that these ants can no longer live without them, since they have lost the will to feed for themselves and, without slaves to feed them, would literally starve to death even in the presence of food. Other species, the pastoral ants, tend "cattle"—aphids which secrete honeydew, a highly prized food of many ants. They protect the aphids from enemies, carry the aphid eggs into their frost-free underground nests in fall and bring them out again in spring to hatch on the aphids' food plants, transfer the mature wingless female aphids to greener feeding grounds, "milk" them of their honeydew, and generally care for their well-being as well as, if not better than, a farmer who takes good care of his cows.

Still other species, the agricultural and harvester ants, practice some kind of agriculture, insofar as they cultivate in their underground nests certain kinds of fungi on which they feed. To provide nourishment for their cultures, they collect bits of leaves which, on their way home, they carry in their mandibles held over their heads, a habit which has given them the name "parasol ants." And when a virgin queen leaves her nest to found a new colony, she takes with her, tucked away within a special hollow below her mouth, a pellet of the fungus to start in her new home a culture of this food supply without which these ants cannot live.

Still other species, the honey ants, have evolved a type of worker whose only purpose in life is to serve as living storage tanks for honey. These so-called "repletes" spend their entire life hanging motionless from the roof of an underground chamber, their bellies extended with honey to bursting-point until they reach the size of large peas, giving up their sweetness when stimulated by other ants. And then there are the so-called thief ants who live a parasitic life of luxury within the nests of other species of ants, from whose wrath they are protected either by an unpleasant odor or by their small size and agility.

Well-known and feared are the South American army and the African driver ants, which, contrary to ordinary ant custom, have no permanent nests but lead a gypsy-like life, camping here today and there tomorrow, killing every living thing in their path, regardless of size, that cannot make good its escape in time, and even driving entire human communities to flight.

Another species, the South American *Camponotus senex,* uses its own larvae, which are able to spin silk, to construct its nests of leaves: while a number of ants pull two leaves together and hold them in this position, others pick up some larvae and gently squeeze them with their mandibles until they secrete the precious liquid silk, which is then used like glue squeezed out of a tube to cement the two leaves together. The nest entrance of the North American *Cryptocerus* is guarded by a special "doorman"—a worker ant whose head is enlarged and shaped like a plug which exactly fits the entrance aperture and, when the "doorman" is in position, closes it as effectively as a cork stoppers a bottle.

111. Head of a paper wasp (*Polistes*). These gentle, unaggressive wasps, which like to build their open nests under the eaves of small buildings and in garages and sheds, sting only in self-defense. Only fecundated queens survive the winter to start a new colony in the spring. The first comb, hanging downward from a short stalk, usually has no more than fifteen to twenty cells, each containing a single egg. From these, grubs hatch and, fed by the mother wasp with bits of captured and shredded insects, grow up, pupate, and emerge as workers ready to help the queen enlarge the comb and care for the next generation of wasps. This "care", however, is not based upon sentimental feelings but upon a mutually beneficial relationship between grub and adult wasp which is called trophallaxis: the grubs, when stimulated by the presence of food, secrete a liquid which the wasps eagerly lap up, and it seems that it is this phenomenon which holds the entire colony together. As summer progresses and food becomes more plentiful, some of the better-fed grubs develop into fully sexed females instead of into sexless workers—they become queens. At the same time, the old queen, by withholding sperm (which she has stored in a special receptacle in her abdomen) and laying unfertilized eggs, begins to produce males, which mate with the young queens. In this way fewer and fewer workers are produced until, finally, the queen stops laying eggs, the workers and male wasps die off, the colony disintegrates, and only the young fertilized queens are left, some of which will survive the winter to start the cycle again next spring.

112. Front view of a tiger beetle (family Cicindelidae). Beetles comprise the largest single order of animals on earth—estimates of the number of different species range to more than a quarter of a million—a fact which testifies to their extraordinary success in their struggle for existence. This success is doubtlessly due to a large degree to one characteristic that distinguishes a beetle from any other kind of insect: the front pair of the two sets of wings is transformed into two hard or tough covers called elytra, which effectively protect not only the delicate hind wings with which the beetle flies but usually also its abdomen. Thus protected, a beetle can dig into the soil, hide under stones, squeeze through narrow cracks, and generally take a higher degree of abuse than most other insects, without losing its ability to fly.

Tiger beetles are great hunters that feed on insects and are thus, with very few exceptions, good fliers. Because of their bright, metallic colors and bold designs, they are a pleasure to the eye.

113. Caterpillar of the silver-spotted skipper (*Epargyreus clarus*). What looks like a pair of huge eyes are not eyes at all but merely eyelike spots which possibly serve to frighten enemies. The real eyes are minute silvery pimples on the side of the

head. "Dummy eyes" of this kind are typical of many other insects or their larvae, such as the caterpillars of the spicebush swallowtail (*Papilio troilus*), the Evemon swallowtail *(Graphium evemon*), and the sphinx moth (family Sphingidae), which has eye-spots on its hind wings; "dummy eyes" also decorate the thorax of the eyed elater (*Alaus oculatus*), which is a large click beetle, and the wings of many butterflies and moths, such as the luna moth (*Actias luna*) and the California silk moth (*Calosaturnia mendocino*), both of which carry eye-spots on the top of the front wings. And they adorn the top of the hind wings of many other moths, such as the polyphemus moth (*Antheraea polyphemus*), the io moth (*Automeris io*), and others.

99-101 ▶

104/105 ▶

◀ 106
107 ▶

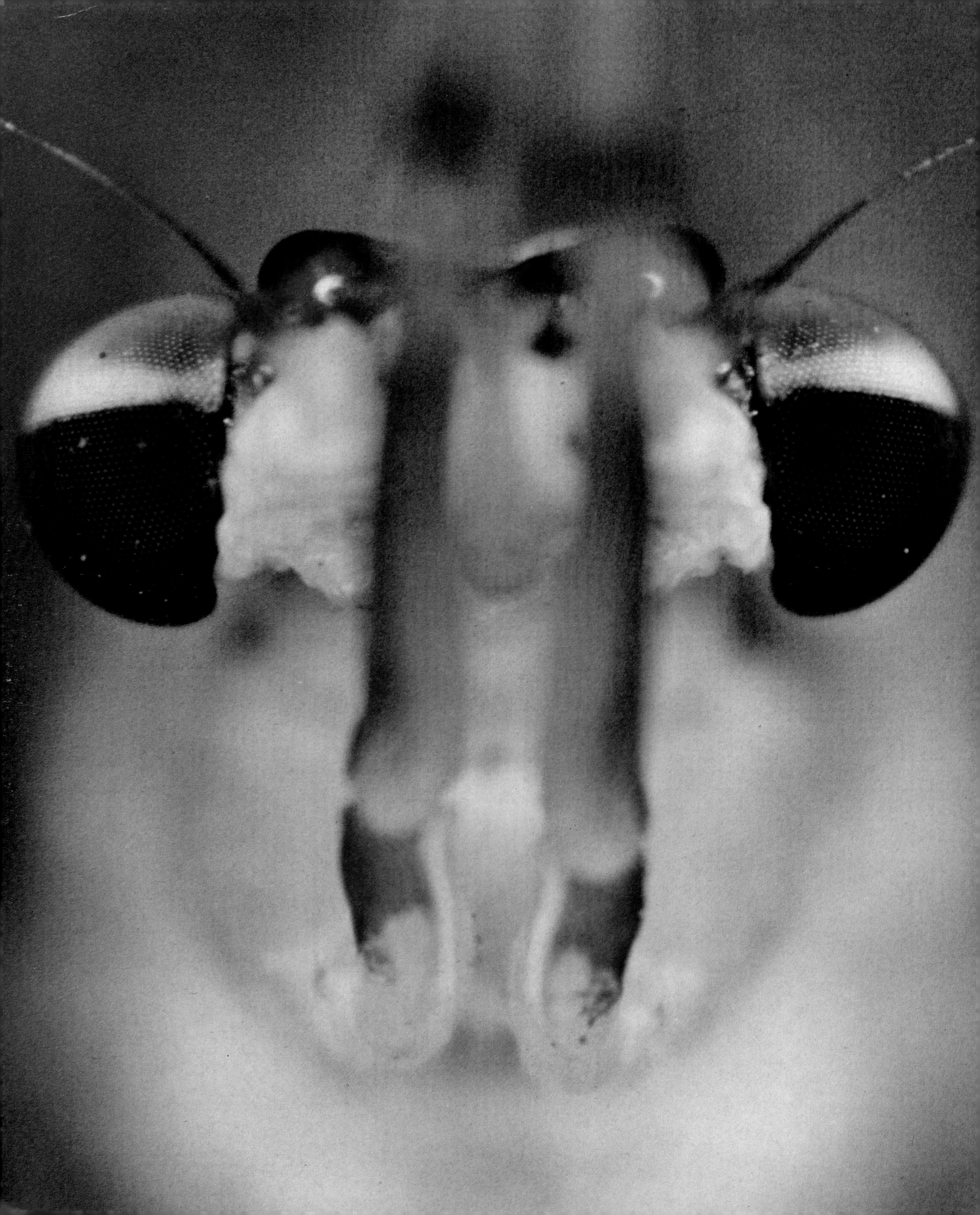

◀108/109

112/113 ▶

X

The Abundance of Life

Life is all-pervading, irrepressible, adaptable to the most exacting environmental conditions. Living organisms thrive at the bottom of the sea in blackest darkness under the unimaginable crushing pressure of more than six miles of water. Others have been found four miles up on the highest mountains on earth, where the air is so rarefied that unprotected man would perish from lack of oxygen; in the desiccating furnace of the desert; in pools of brine and oil; in the scalding waters of volcanic springs, and in the bone-chilling cold of polar snow and ice.

But despite this seemingly complete penetration, life covers the earth only in the manner of a skin—an incredibly thin layer that on land extends downward only as far as the roots of the deepest-growing trees and upward as high as the tops of the tallest trees. For, although flying birds and insects ascend high into the air, they must return to the ground. Even in the oceans, the overwhelming majority of all marine life is confined to a zone that extends from the surface to a depth of hardly five hundred feet. This thin layer of life is called the biosphere.

But although it is thin, this layer is home to an estimated one million different species of animals and some 375,000 species of plants. And since all these organisms compete for the same raw materials—carbon, nitrogen, oxygen, phosphorus, calcium, magnesium, and a comparatively small number of other elements and chemical compounds such as water—the resulting competition is unbelievably fierce and only the best adapted and strongest survive.

To compete successfully in the struggle for existence, living organisms rely primarily upon two mechanisms: adaptation and numbers. All living things are, to a greater or lesser degree, adapted to one specific way of life under specific conditions; such animals or plants are said to "occupy a specific niche" within their biotic community, with no immediate competitors outside their own species. It is a biological impossibility for two or more different species of either animals or plants to lead exactly the same kind of life (i. e. to fill the same niche) within the same area because, invariably, one will become dominant and the others will be forced to move out or become extinct.

To assure the continuance of their species, most plants produce an incredible number of seeds of which only a minute percentage ever develops, and the progeny of many animals is staggering—generally the more so, the "lower" the order to which the respective species belongs. A large puffball—a fungus shaped like a small white football—for example, can contain up to seven thousand billion spores, yet of this unimaginable number perhaps only one in a trillion will mature. And a single ordinary oyster is capable of spawning a hundred million eggs. What would result if all these organisms were to grow up, reach maturity, and propagate can be gauged from the fact that if all the offspring of a single pair of flies were to survive, interbreed, and multiply for the duration of only one single year, the resulting mass of flies, tightly packed, would fill a sphere ninety-six million miles in diameter, which is more than the distance from the earth to the sun.

How enormous the pressure of life is, and how true the old proverb which says that nature abhors a vacuum was made abundantly clear by a spectacular event that occurred in 1883 when, with a force equal to that of a ten-thousand-megaton hydrogen bomb, the island of Krakatoa near Java blew up as the result of a volcanic explosion. This blast, which pulverized six cubic miles of rock and completely blanketed what remained of the island with a solid layer of pumice and ash, also obliterated, of course, every trace of life. So complete was extinction that, nine months later, the only sign of life which a visiting naturalist

◀ 114

found was a single lonely spider blown by the wind across the twenty-five miles of sea which separate Krakatoa from the nearest land. Three years later, however, colonization by life had already begun: fifteen species of flowering plants and eleven ferns were found. Twenty-five years later, the count was 263 species of animals including sixteen species of birds and two species of reptiles. And less than fifty years after its destruction and sterilization the island was again inhabited by forty-seven species of vertebrates and hundreds of insects, and covered with a dense blanket of vegetation.

114. An aggregate of edible common mussels (*Mytilus*) of all ages from juveniles to adults, attached to a rock off the shore of Cape Cod by fine but strong, horny threads (byssus) which these mollusks secrete.

115. Serpulid worms (*Spirorbis*) attached to kelp. Although they look like snails, these animals are not mollusks but worms (class Polychaeta) which secrete and live in limy coiled tubes. If one looks closely at this picture, one can discover smaller shells among the larger ones, tiny ones among the smaller, and minute ones next to these—and still there are many more too small to be immediately visible to the eye. And yet this photograph records only a few square inches of a beach many miles long.

116. A close look at the fierce competition among the weeds that populate a drainage ditch in Connecticut. The plant shown in the picture at the top, right, is poison ivy.

117. A shoot of the skunk cabbage rolled tightly into a tube suitable to break through frosty ground, heralds spring in a New England wood.

115 - 117 ▶

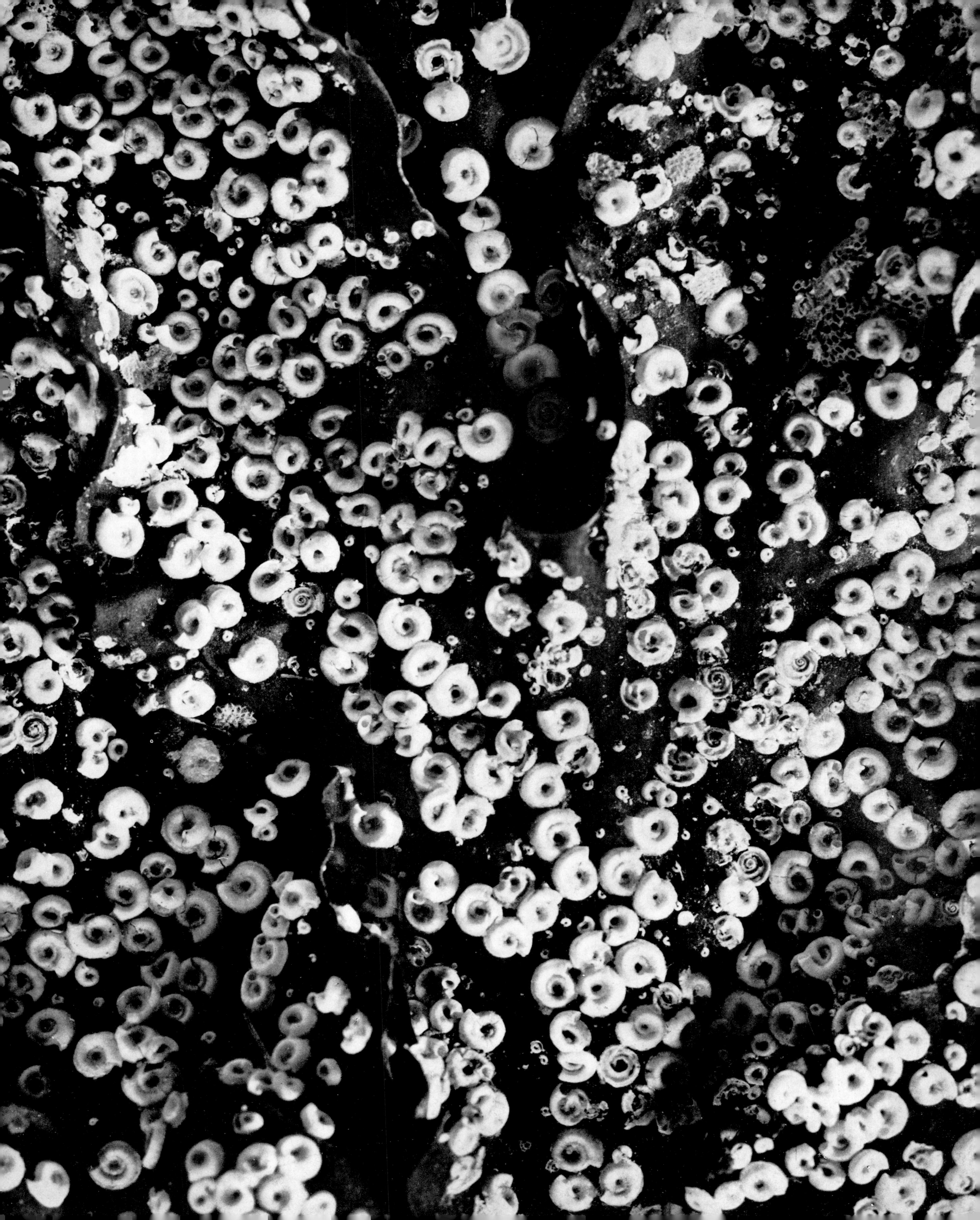

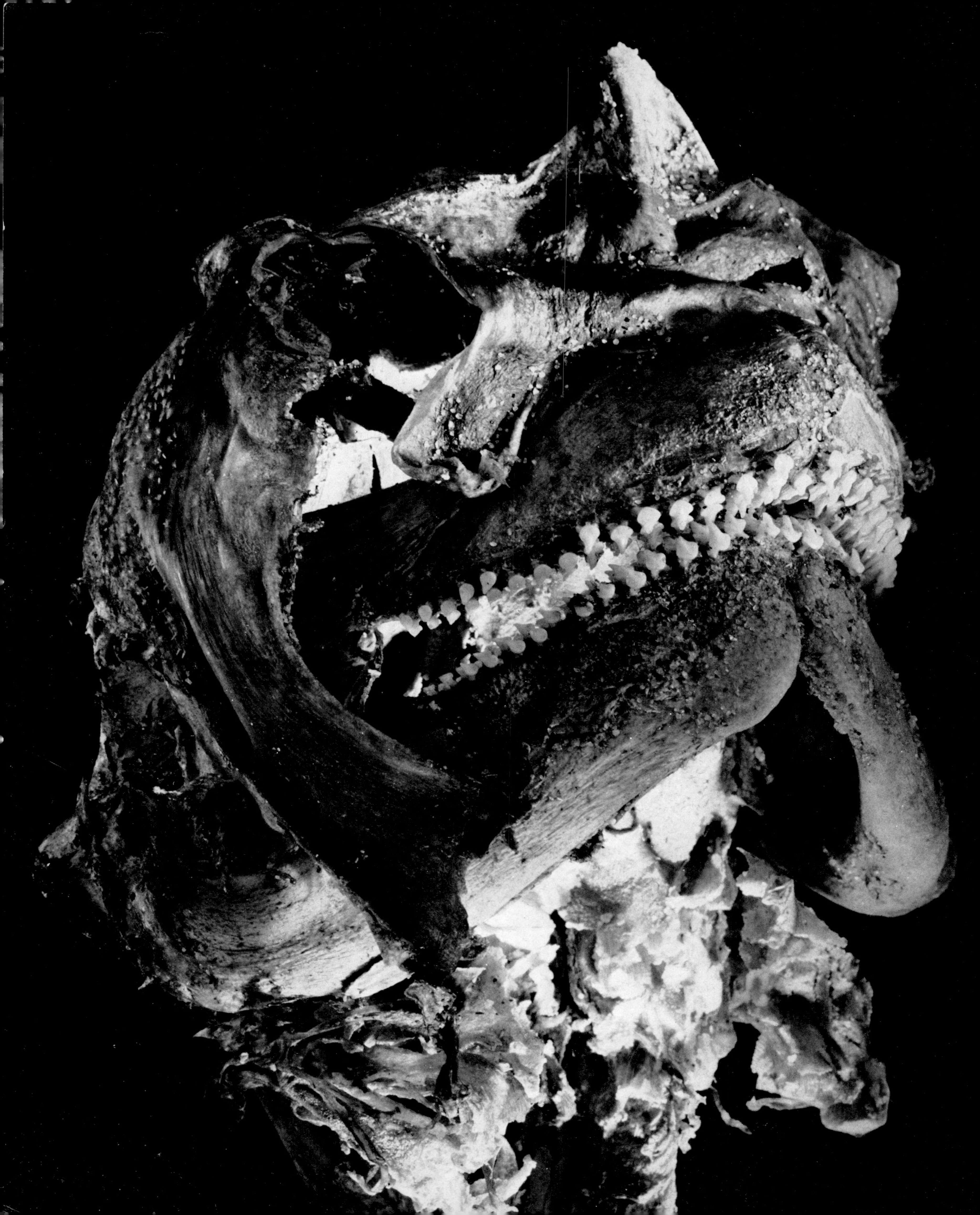

XI

Dying and Death

One of the strongest instincts in man and animal is to preserve and prolong his or its own life. During the Middle Ages alchemists even went so far in the quest for physical immortality that they spent endless hours concocting the strangest and often most unappetizing mixtures in an effort to find the "elixir of life"—a potion that would make him who drank it immortal. Little did they think about—or care—what would happen should they succeed: a world suffocating under masses of writhing human bodies suffering all the agonies of hell after they had consumed all the available food.

Death, for two obvious reasons, is an inevitable prerequisite for life: because space on earth is limited and, should no living creature ever die, there would soon be "standing room only;" and because not only the available food resources but also those of the raw material of which living things are made are likewise restricted and sufficient in quantity only for a limited number of individuals, be they microbes, mice, or men. To what unspeakable horrors physical immortality would lead is amply made clear by Fremlin's projection of the "population explosion" (see page 15) and the unrestricted propagation of flies (see page 53) of which I spoke before. Death is the price we have to pay for the privilege of living.

For, as I see it, life is a privilege, a gift bestowed upon us at the expense of other living things—the animals and plants that give us our food. So that we may live, others must die—the steers and sheep and swine, chicken and turkeys, lobsters and clams; the grains of wheat and corn that will never become plants, and countless other living things—because it is their substance we need to build our tissues and fuel our energy.

Eat and be eaten is the basic law of nature which ecologists—biologists whose field is the study of the mutual relationship between living organisms and their environment—have arrived at in the concept of the "food chain" or "food pyramid" which, perhaps, is best explained by an example: a thousand pounds of plankton—myriads of minute, passively floating or weakly swimming, primitive plants and animals living in the sea—if eaten by the creatures that feed on them, produce some hundred pounds of crustaceans, mollusks, and tiny fish; these hundred pounds of assorted creatures, eaten in turn by larger fish, are converted into some ten pounds of fish meat; finally, predatory fish or man, eating ten pounds of fish, will gain approximately one pound in weight. Thus, in this example, it is the plankton that forms the bottom, and large predatory fish that have no enemies, or man, that form the top of the "food pyramid," in which transfer of the "raw material," from one step to the next involves an approximately ten-to-one loss in weight. Another food chain might start with a mosquito which is eaten by a dragonfly which is snapped up by a frog which is devoured by a snake which falls prey to a hawk.

It may seem as if man, large predatory fish, and hawks (and, of course, many other animals such as lions, bears, and eagles) which have no enemies that feed on them, might well be the end of their particular food chain. This is not true, however, for all animals are host to a number of parasites that feed on them while they are alive, and they provide food for other animals—scavengers, maggots, microbes—when dead. Whether we are buried or cremated, we cannot prevent the basic chemicals of which our bodies consist from recirculating and being used again by the animals and plants that come after us—a form of reincarnation. The carbon that forms the nucleus of our cells and the calcium within our bones may well have been part of a dinosaur or prehistoric man (and certainly was part of all the animals we eat in our lives), and the nitrogen and phosphorus in our bodies part of plants living millions of years ago (as well as those we had for dinner yesterday). To me, this is a very profound truth because it makes me realize how closely we are related to the animals and plants and how much we belong to the world in which we live. We are indestructible. We are immortal. We are of the Universe.

Although we know that every living thing must die, we know very little about the mechanism of the clock that runs down in all of us, and why it cannot go on ticking forever. Why is it possible that a tree—a sequoia, a bristlecone pine—can live three thousand years and more but not ten thousand, or a hundred thousand, or indefinitely? And if a sequoia can live three thousand years, why not a maple? Or a man? After all, the body constantly renews itself—up to a point; why not forever? We do not know—but we know that this is for the good of all. Each of us is given his time—a time to live, to enjoy life, to propagate his kind, and see life perpetuated in his children. It is for our children's and children's children's sake that we must die.

However, organisms exist which, at least potentially, are immortal. These are certain unicellular protozoans that propagate asexually by simple cell division (binary fission). Unless killed accidentally or eaten by an enemy, these microbes never die but can, at least theoretically, go on living forever.

118. This gruesome-looking object is the decaying head of a skate, a fish related to the rays and sharks, washed up one night on the beach near Montauk Point, Long Island.

119. Windrows of shells, mostly of hardshell and surf clams but also of moon snails, scallops, whelks, and other kinds, litter the sands of Jones Beach near New York.

120. Riddled by the tunnels of wood-boring beetles and crumbling in decay, a giant pine has fallen in death in the forest of the Kaibab Plateau, Arizona.

121. The remains of a horse — a grass-eating animal which in death gives back its borrowed substance to the soil to provide nutrients and minerals to future generations of grassy plants of the kind to which it owed its life—slowly sinking into the ground on a New Mexican desert.

119-121 ▶

XII

The Skeleton

Any animal that possesses an internal skeleton—no matter whether complete or incomplete, whether it consists of bone or cartilage—is a member of the phylum Chordata, which is subdivided into six divisions with a total of some forty thousand different species: the mammals, birds, reptiles, amphibians, fishes, and invertebrate chordates. The latter, to be sure, are represented only by a few hundred small marine animals (sea squirts, lancelets, and salps) which are characterized by the possession of a notochord—a stiffening rod consisting of a fibrous sheath surrounding a string of liquid-filled pressurized cells which provides both firmness and flexibility and represents the forerunner of a genuine inner skeleton.

A skeleton fulfills three major functions: it provides firmness combined with flexibility and articulation in an animal's body; it gives protection to certain vital organs such as brain, heart, and lungs; and it offers surfaces to which muscles and tendons can be attached.

A skeleton reflects, of course, an animal's form and habits. The skeletons of flying animals—bats or flying birds (for there are flightless birds too—the ostriches, emus, kiwis, penguins, and others)—always consist of thin and often hollow bones, that is to say *light* bones, since weight is, of course, an important consideration in the construction of any flying machine. On the other hand, the bones of animals that are of sluggish habits or live in water, where weight is therefore of little or no concern, are generally massive and thick. But much more subtle characteristics of an animal's form, behavior, or habits are reflected in the construction and shape of its bones. From the form of certain bones of the precursors of man, for example, anthropologists can tell whether the respective creatures were still shuffling around like apes or already walking upright like man. As a matter of fact, so revealing and logical is the structure of bones that paleontologists—experts in comparative anatomy whose specialize in the study of life in past geological periods—can often reconstruct, at least in regard to its main characteristics, the appearance and habits of entire animals, extinct perhaps millions of years ago, from the shape of single fossil bones, bone fragments, or teeth.

Bones have an inherent sculptural quality which, in its pure and elemental form, is akin to the best in modern abstract sculpture. They are functional in the truest sense of the word, combining maximum strength with minimum weight and expenditure of material. Joined to form skeletal units, bones provide rigidity combined with flexibility and delicate articulation, linked together in the form of structures that make use of the same engineering principles as hinges and roller bearings, ball-and-socket joints, cantilevered structures, suspension bridges, vaulted roofs, and prestressed concrete shells. Their smoothly rounded and often highly complex shapes are a delight to behold and a pleasure to touch.

As I write these lines, I have in front of me the skull of a woodchuck (*Marmota monax*), which I found on my grounds. It must have been exposed to sunshine and rain for quite a time because it is weathered to the point where all its sutures have opened up, so that, when I gently shake it in the palm of my hand, it gives forth a dry rattle. But despite this obvious looseness, it does not fall apart because each individual piece of bone is joined to its neighbors with dovetailed interlocking seams of the most exquisite design. The movement of the finest watch, examined under magnification, seems rough and crude when compared to these tiny bits of bone and the utter precision with which they are finished and fitted together. The following photographs will, I hope, convey an idea of the deep satisfaction which the study of bones—some of nature's structurally and aesthetically most perfect forms—can evoke in the contemplative mind.

◀122

122. The skeletons of a horse and a man, for easy comparison mounted together in identical stance, clearly show both the similarities resulting from their common origin and the differences caused by adaptation to dissimilar ways of life: the horse, as the construction of its legs and feet indicates, is specially adapted to running; man, possessing a relatively unspecialized skeleton, is fit to adapt himself to many ways of life.

123. Skeleton of a herring gull (*Larus argentatus*) mounted in flying position. Its bones are light and thin to conserve weight. The ribs are reinforced and joined firmly to the keel-like breastbone, which, eggshell-thin for lightness, T-shaped in cross-section and thickened along the edges for maximum rigidity, provides the large surfaces necessary for the attachment of the powerful flight muscles characteristic of these birds. The wing is a modified forearm, and the remnants of a thumb can still be seen.

124. A comparison between the skeleton of a 1/10-ounce hummingbird (*Calypte anna*) and the femur of an extinct flightless thousand pound elephant bird (*Aepyornis maximus*) dramatically illustrates the enormous span between the smallest and the largest bird.

125. *Top*: The close-up of the weathered jawbone of a cow, shown here in approximately six times linear magnification, reveals the structure of this bone as it slowly disintegrates under the influences of water, sun, and frost.

Bottom: The close-up of a suture of a human skull illustrates how an intricate interlocking construction dovetails plate to plate.

126—127. Each of these three skeletons belongs to a highly specialized animal which is admirably adapted to one particular way of life.

Top: The skeleton of an African hero shrew (*Scutisorex congicus*) shows a spine which, arched and given additional strength by the interlocking prongs of its vertebrae, is able to support without ill effects the weight of a man—perhaps an advantage to this little creature which hunts for insects and grubs in the forest litter, where it might be stepped on accidentally by larger animals.

Left: The skeleton of a pygmy armadillo (*Zeadyus pichiy*) clearly shows the armored tail-plate, attached to its hip bones, which protects this animal from the rear when, pursued by an enemy, it dives head first into its burrow, sealing the hole as effectively as a stopper plugs a pipe.

Right: The skeleton of a triggerfish (*Balistes capriscus*) is equipped with an unusual device: its first three dorsal fin spines are modified in such a way that the fish can snap up the first spine and lock it in position with the second, so that it can serve at will either as a defense against being swallowed by a bigger fish, or to anchor its body firmly in a crevice of the coral reef where it hides and thus make it impossible for an enemy to dislodge it.

128. Skeleton of fruit bat (*Rousettus collaris*) or flying fox, well adapted for flight: to conserve weight, its limb bones are delicate and hollow and the skull bones almost paper-thin. To support the membranous wings, the fingers and heel bones are enormously elongated. The entire structure is not unlike that of a kite constructed of slender staves covered with paper except that it is extremely flexible.

129. Designed for tension rather than compression, this is the skeleton of a three-toed sloth (genus Bradypus), an animal which spends its entire life in an upside-down position in trees. Its long limbs, which end in enormous claws, are perfectly adapted for grasping branches and hold the animal securely even when it sleeps upside down.

123 ▶

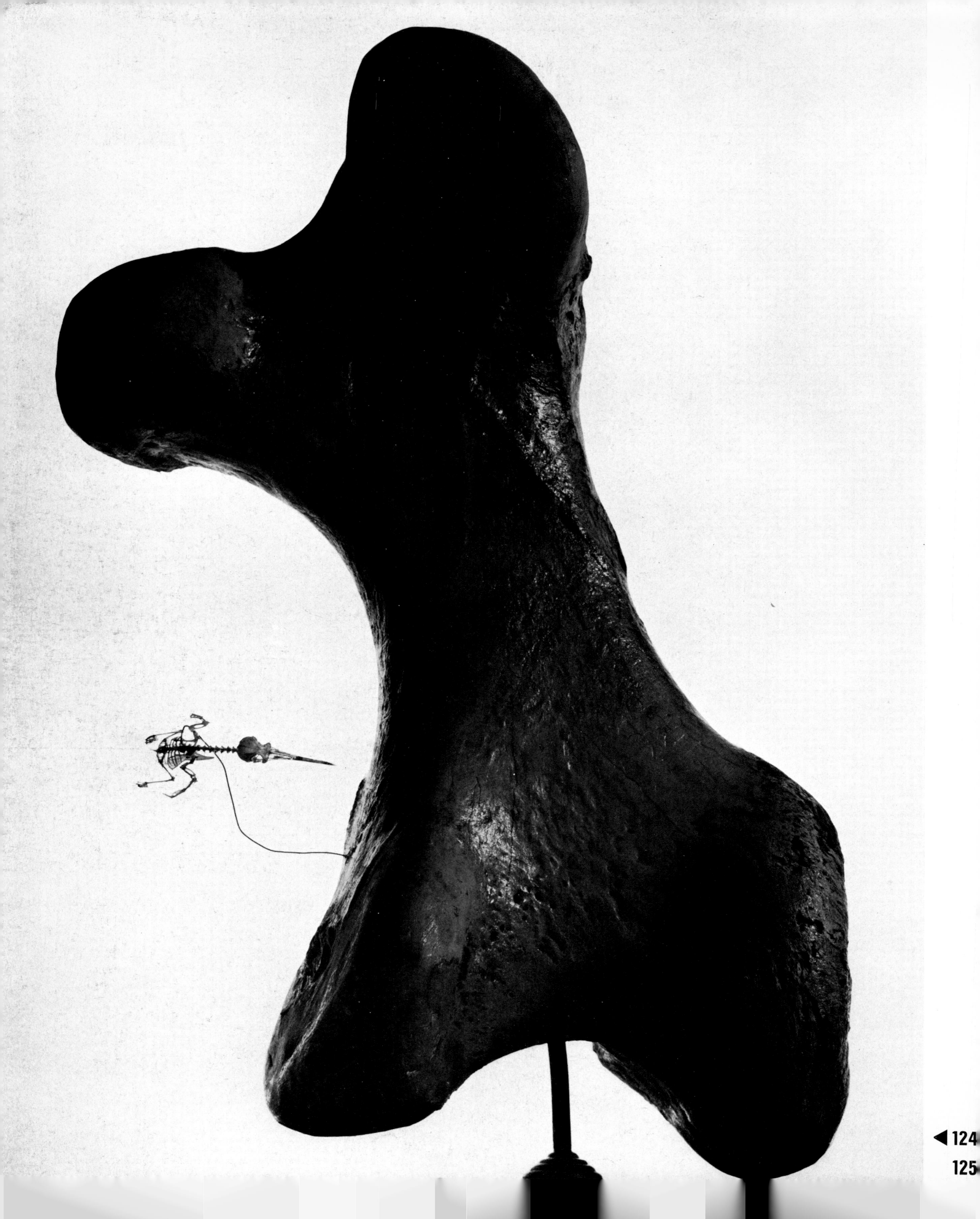

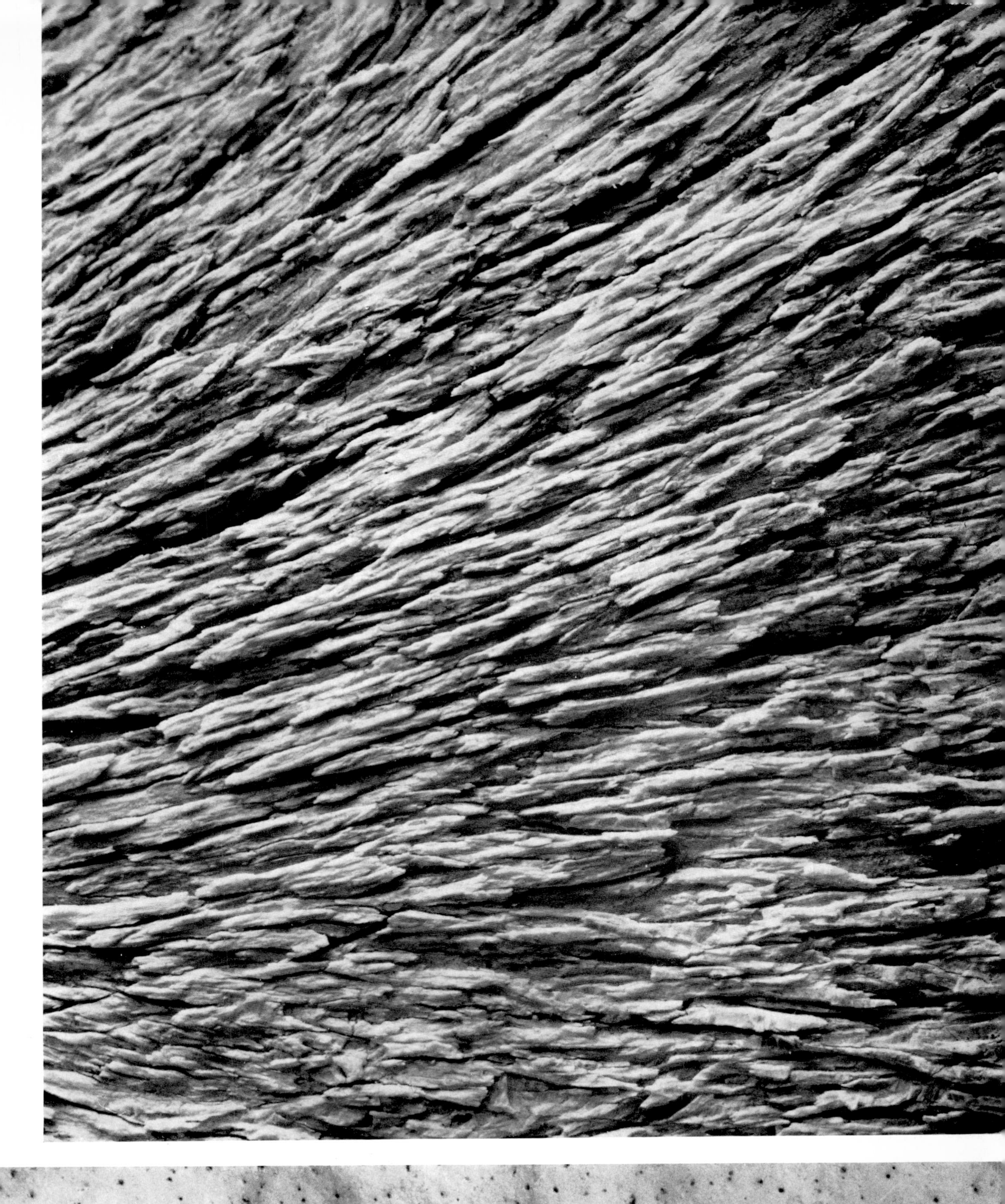

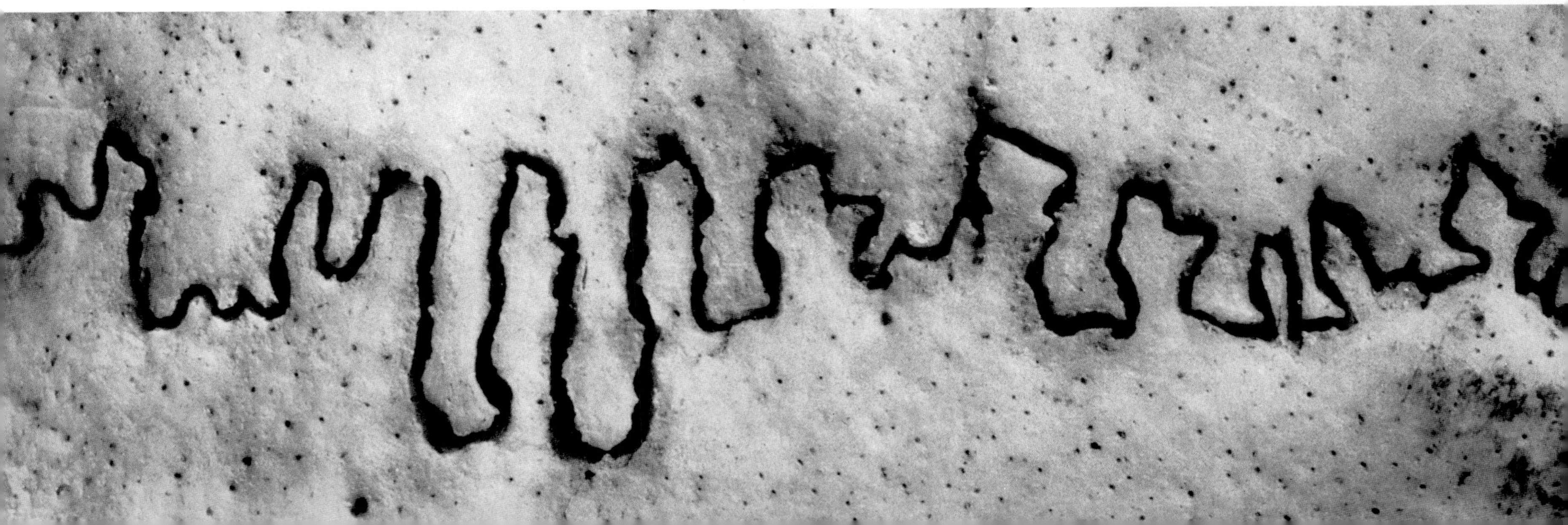

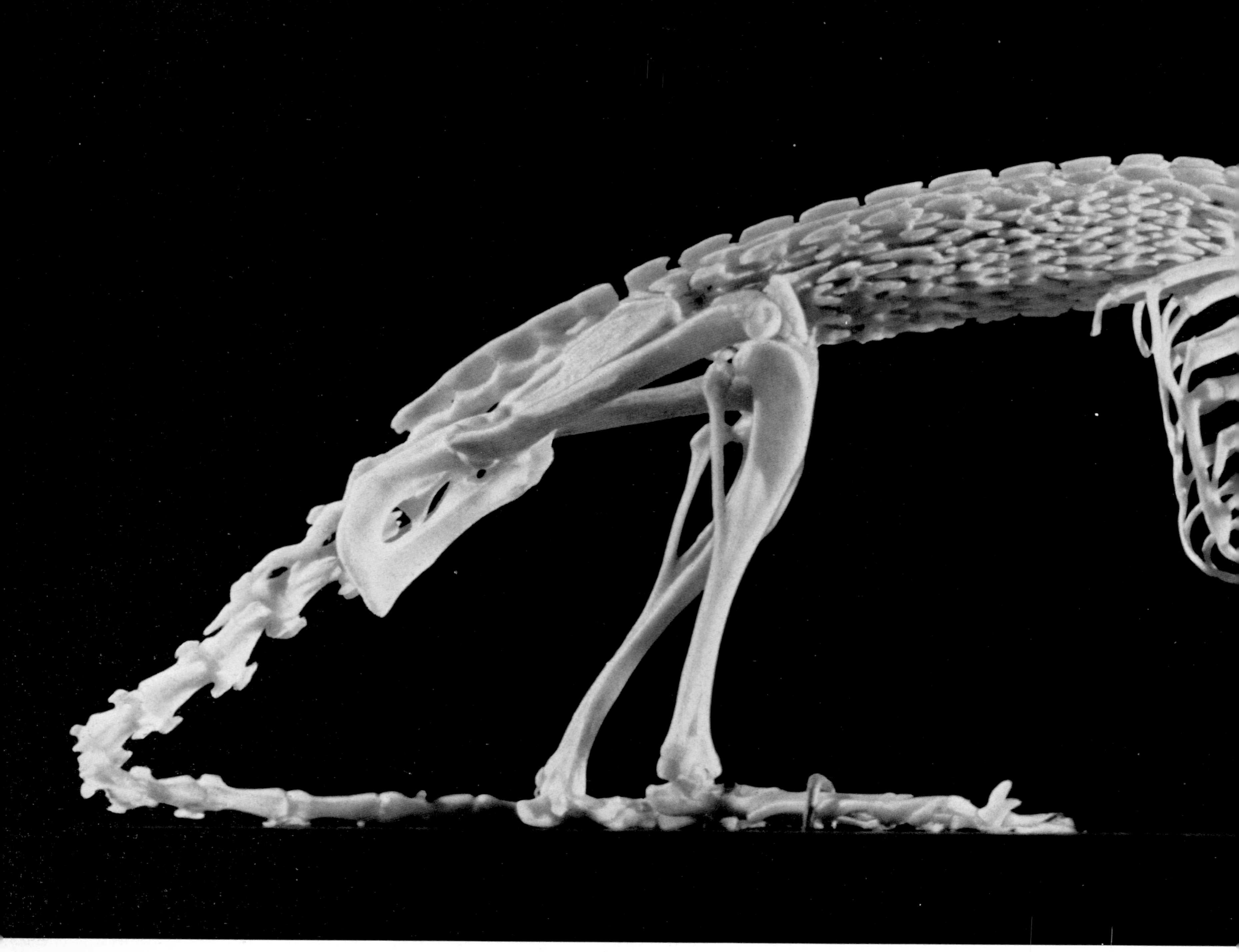

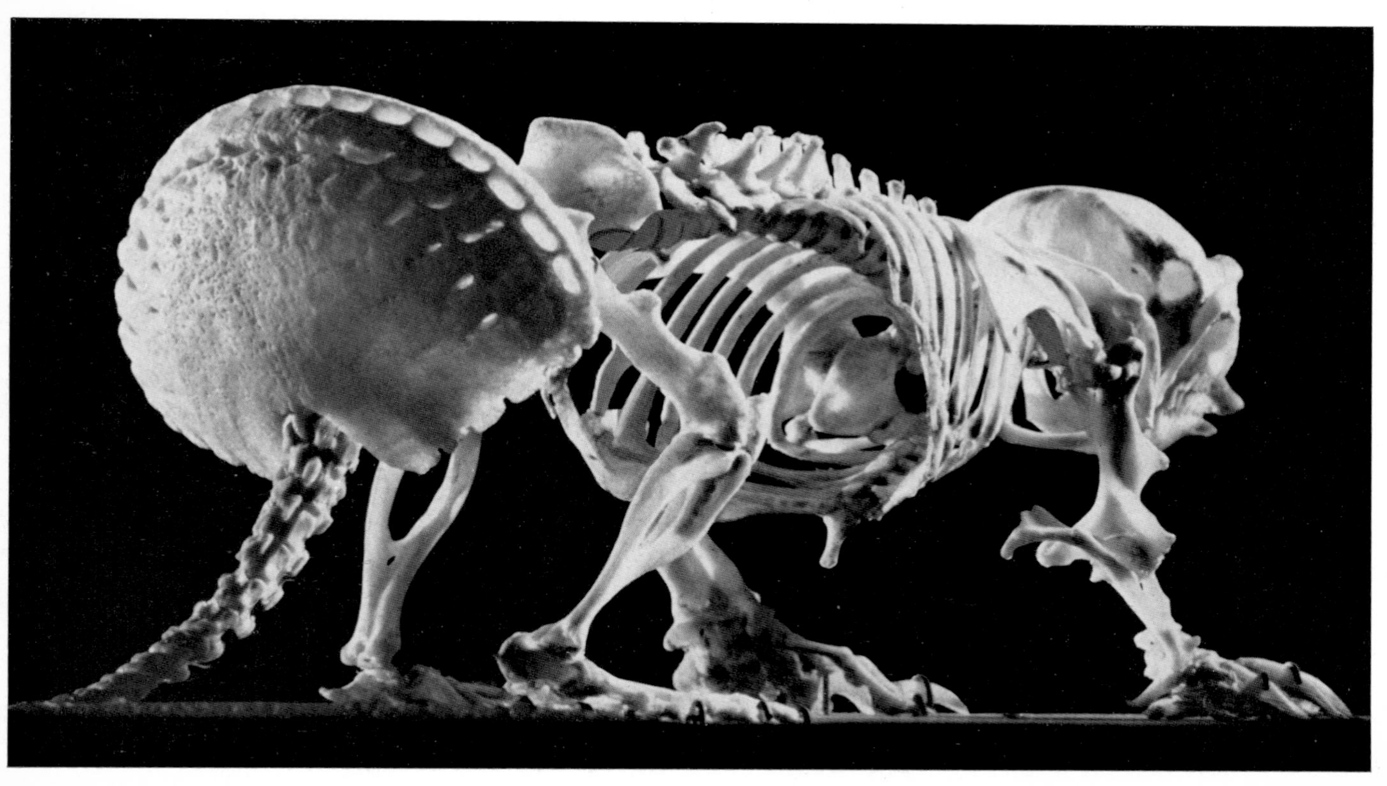

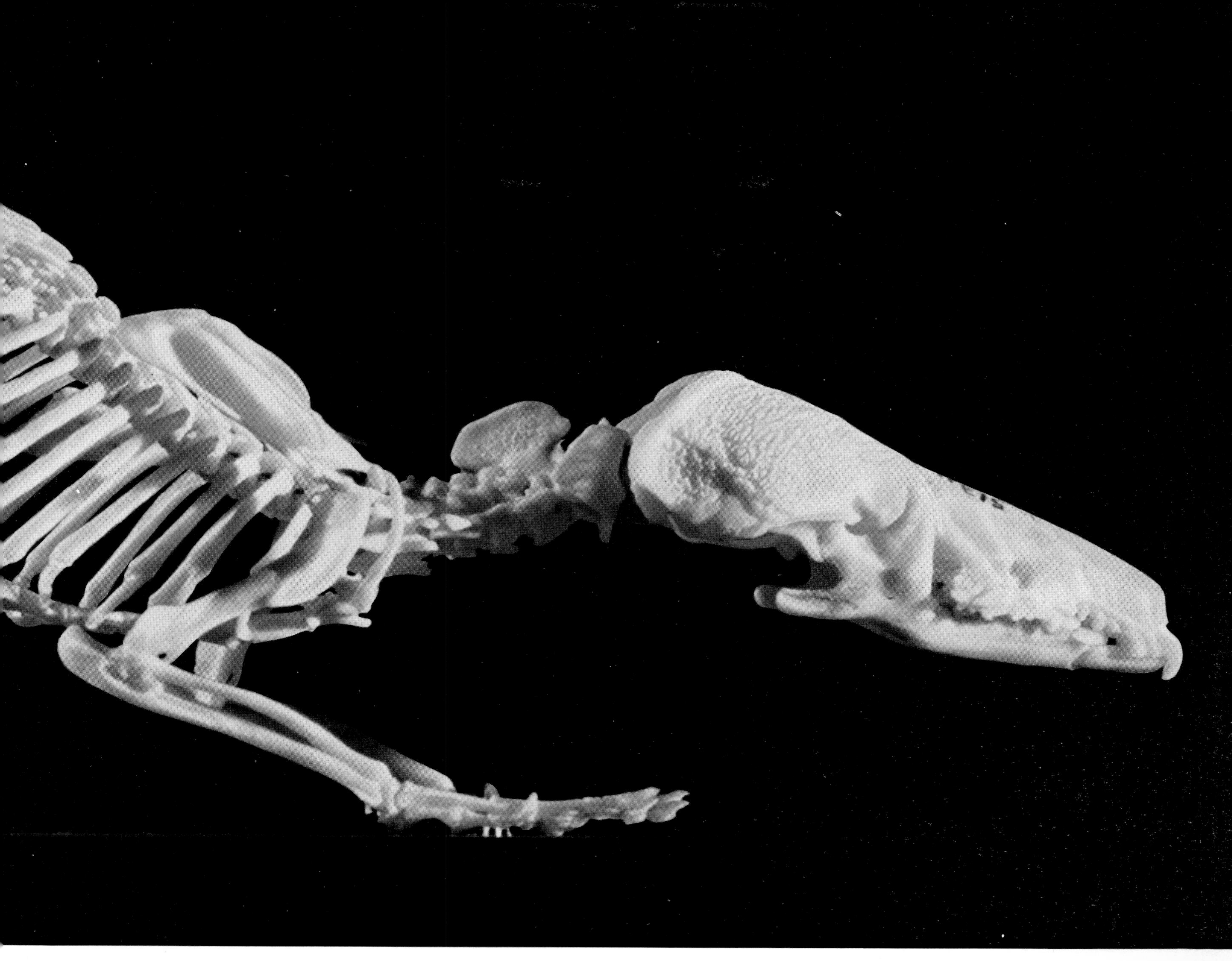

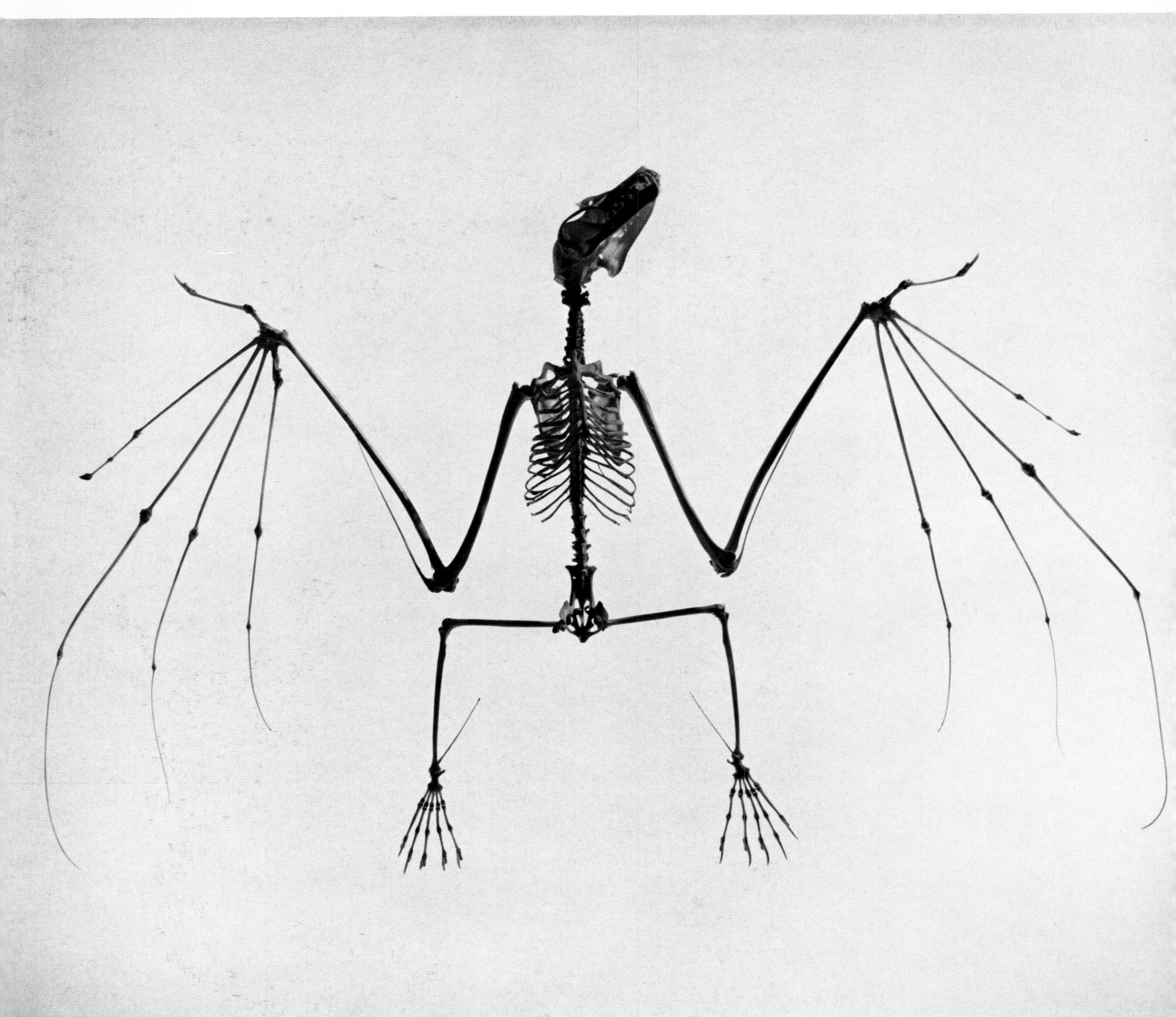

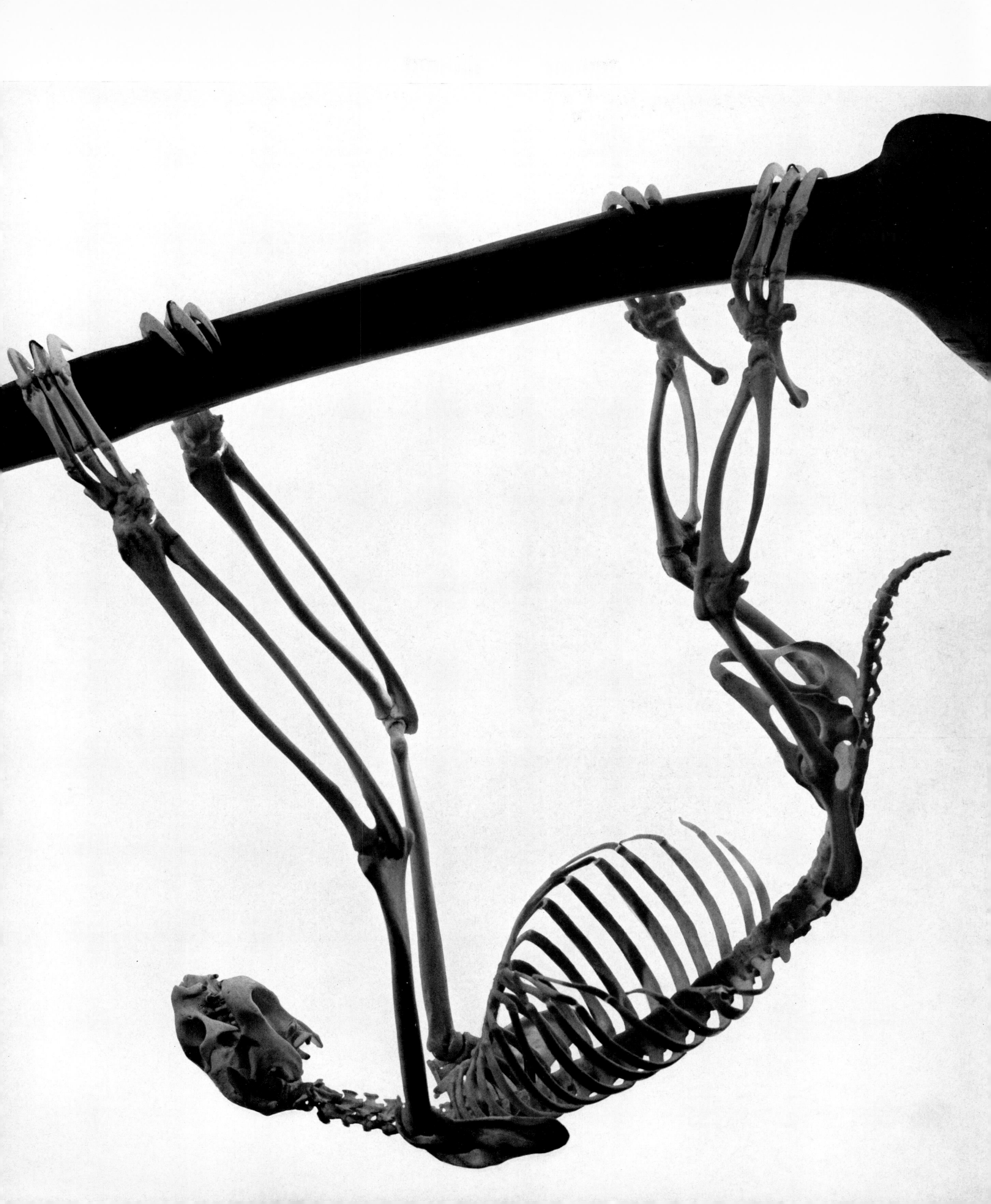

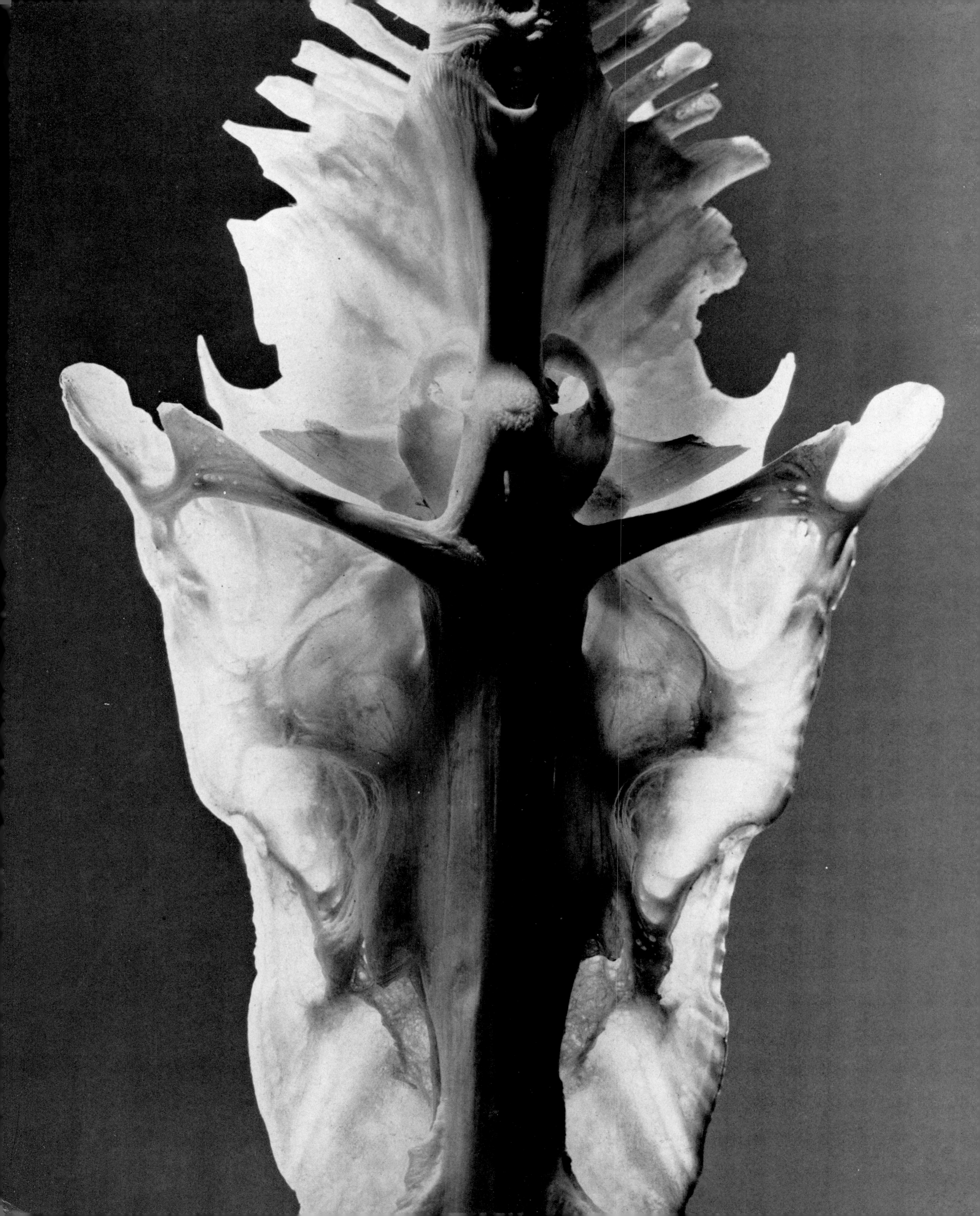

XIII

Bone Specialization

Although the shapes of bones are infinitely varied, they might be considered as variations of only four basic types: long, tubular bones like those of the arms and legs; flat bones like those of the skull, shoulderblades, pelvis, and ribs; the relatively small, delicately formed bones of the vertebrae; and small but compact bones like those of the middle foot and wrist.

Out of these few basic types, however, resourceful nature has created the skeletons of all the mammals, birds, reptiles, amphibians, and fishes, each modified and refined in accordance with the requirements of the respective species of animal. How great these modifications within the same type of bone or assembly of bones can be is forcefully brought to mind if one compares, for example, the skulls of an elephant, a dog, and a hummingbird, all of which are modifications of the same basic structure. Or the hand of a man, the wing of a bird, the flipper of a whale, and the wing of a bat, the skeletal parts of which, too, are merely variations of the same design adapted to suit the needs of their owners. The following pictures show some of these variations in detail.

130. Skull of a crucifix catfish. The reinforcing ridges and braces which superficially resemble the figure of Christ on the cross gave this fish its name.

131. Skull of a gorilla. The great sagittal crest with its large areas for muscle attachment and the supraorbital tori (bony arches) which provide further points of attachment for muscles in addition to serving as protectors for the eyes, as well as the prognathous jaw, give this skull its ferocious expression. However, to evaluate an object of nature in anthropomorphic terms is usually misleading—the skull of a gorilla was not designed to frighten man, but assumed its form as the evolutionary result of adaptation to the physical and environmental requirements of gorillas.

132—133. Shown here are the skulls of nine different species of chordates, each based upon and evolved from the same original design, yet each an adaptation to a specific way of life. For easy comparison, they are here reproduced in identical scale.

Top left: Skull of a fox—a carnivore, a flesh-eating mammal—has teeth that are adapted to its special feeding habits: pointed dagger-like canines for holding and killing animals; sharp, scissors-like carnassials (last upper premolars and first lower molars) for shearing and tearing flesh.

Center left: Skull of a cat—a carnivore related to the lions, tigers, jaguars, etc.—has a shorter face than that of a fox but teeth that are similarly adapted to killing animals and shearing flesh.

Bottom left: Skull of an insect-eating mammal—an animal belonging to the same order as the moles, hedgehogs, and shrews—has dentition that is specially adapted to catching and chopping up insects: some teeth are needlepointed for holding, others scissors-like for shearing, still others flat-crowned for crushing. Certain living insectivores still resemble very closely some of the most ancient fossil mammals known, having changed relatively little in one hundred and fifty million years. One of these little fossil creatures may very well have been a direct ancestor of man, and so strong is the evidence that some investigators now consider the tree-shrews—animals which previously had been classified as insectivores—to be members of the primates, the order to which man belongs.

Top center: Skull of a beaver—a rodent related to the squirrels, hamsters, mice, etc.—is typical of animals that are highly adapted to gnawing: the incisor teeth are very big and strong (in fox and cat they are very small) and canine teeth (the most prominent teeth of carnivores), for which rodents have no use, are lacking.

◀ 130

Center: Skull of an antelope—a hoofed mammal with an even number of toes—is typical of ruminant or cud-chewing animals: the upper incisors are absent; the lower incisors and canines are modified to form a cropping mechanism, biting against a pad in the upper jaw.

Bottom center: Skull of an owl—a carnivorous night-flying bird. Its shape reflects the way of life of owls: like all nocturnal animals, they have unusually large eyes because large eyes gather more light than small ones. These huge eyes in turn require unusually large sockets, which are further augmented by bony rings for added protection of the eyes. And being flesh eaters, owls need a strong, sharp, hooklike beak to kill their prey and tear off bits of its flesh.

Top right: Skull of a spiny ant eater—an egg-laying mammal living in Tasmania and New Guinea—has evolved in adaptation to the habits of those animals, which live on a diet of termites and ants. They possess a wormlike, very long tongue smeared with sticky saliva with which they lap up the insects that adhere to it, swallowing them whole. Teeth are therefore not needed, and consequently, the jaw muscles are extremely weak and require no special ridges for their attachment to the skull. This accounts for its smoothly rounded form.

Center right: Skull of a dolphin—a marine mammal related to the whales. All the teeth in its sawlike, unusually long jaws are very much alike and adapted to seizing and manipulating slippery fish, which are not chewed but swallowed whole.

Bottom right: Skull of a loon—a diving bird—has a long and streamlined beak adapted to underwater swimming. Loons live on fish, in the pursuit of which they dive to depths of 160 feet and more; they can stay under water for as long as a quarter of an hour, during which time they may travel two miles or more.

134—135. Skeleton of a Gaboon viper. One hundred and thirty-three pairs of hinged ribs forming a flattened articulated bony tube protect the soft body of this four-foot long reptile and support the powerful muscles with which it moves and strikes at its prey. Exquisitely shaped in every detail, this skeleton tapers gracefully toward both ends of the snake.

136. Skeletal engineering—examples of "convergence" in the evolutionary development of two totally unrelated animals: above, longitudinal section of the upper wing bone (humerus) of an eagle—a bird, a member of the phylum Chordata; below, a view into the shell of a horseshoe "crab" (*Limulus polyphemus*)—a member of the phylum *Arthropoda* and a distant relative of the scorpions and spiders. In both structures, struts and braces serve to stiffen and reinforce certain skeletal parts to achieve maximum strength with a minimum expenditure of material—similar needs produced strikingly similar forms as the result of a process which is called "convergent adaptation."

137. The pelvis of a three-toed sloth—a tree-climbing mammal—employs the principle of the closed ringlike arch to achieve strength through form and lightness through elimination of material in places where it is not needed—the holes in the side plates. It is constructed as though it were designed according to the latest engineering theories.

138. Sectioned elephant skull. Because the powerful muscles needed to move the heavy head and trunk require large areas for attachment, the skull must be big enough to provide these surfaces; and to make this big skull as light as possible, its bones are not solid but honeycombed wherever structural requirements permit.

139. Vertebrate bones are marvels of functional engineering, combining strength and lightness in the most economical way, as illustrated by these examples: at the top, magnified six times linear, a vertebra of an anglerfish; at the left, a section through the upper end of the femur of a large mammal. In both, the organization of the fine structure of their substance mirrors the pattern of stress and strain to which they are subjected. At the right, the cross-section of a femur shows its

tubular construction which is based upon the well-known engineering principle which states that, equality of mass and weight provided, a tube is stronger than a solid rod.

140. The backbone of a fish is a strong yet supple structure which protects the spinal cord and supports the great locomotor muscles. Dorsal and ventral processes increase the strength of the spinal column.

141. The pelvic complex of a bird (pelican)—the foundation of its entire skeleton—is a thin-shelled structure reinforced by the fused bones of the spine and braced by struts like the keel of a ship for utmost rigidity, feather-light yet extremely strong.

142—143. A vertebrate's vital organs are encased in bony armor—the rib cage (which also serves as an air pump for breathing) shielding heart and lungs, the skull protecting the brain. Here too the structural design ingeniously combines lightness and strength, as evidenced in the transluminated monkey skull: strong arched ridges reinforce the bony shell in strategic places, and thick bracing "beams"—zones where new bone is deposited as the shell expands in growth—strengthen the skull along the lines of juncture of its plates.

144—145. Skeletal articulation in vertebrates is mainly based upon the principle of rotary motion: most of the bones are joined in such a way that movement is essentially circular, the bone rotating about a stationary hingelike or ball-and-socket joint. More complicated movements of limbs—hands, feet, or wings—are produced through a combination of several rotary motions by several joints. In swimming or slithering vertebrates, motion is primarily based upon hingelike bone articulation in combination with the sliding of vertebrae against one another, resulting in the typical sinuous movements of snakes and fish.

Two views through the heel joint of a horse (plate 144) show the same structure in two different sections, one rotated ninety degress in relation to the other. The heel bone is at the left. The bone substance is organized along the lines of prevailing stress. The twin grooves make this a very strong and inflexible joint that excludes wobbling and permits rotation in only a single plane—normally an advantage to a fast-running animal but a potentially disastrous quality should the animal fall into a hole.

145. *Top:* The movement of the human forearm around the hingelike elbow joint shown in multiple exposure. The (here stationary) humerus (upper arm bone) is at the right; the radius and ulna (bones of the forearm) are shown in four different positions. The radius (the upper bone at the left side of the picture) can also be rotated in relation to the ulna to turn the palm of the hand up or down.

Bottom: The ball-and-socket joint of the human hip, in which the head of the femur swivels within a socket in the pelvis, provides for a high degree of articulation.

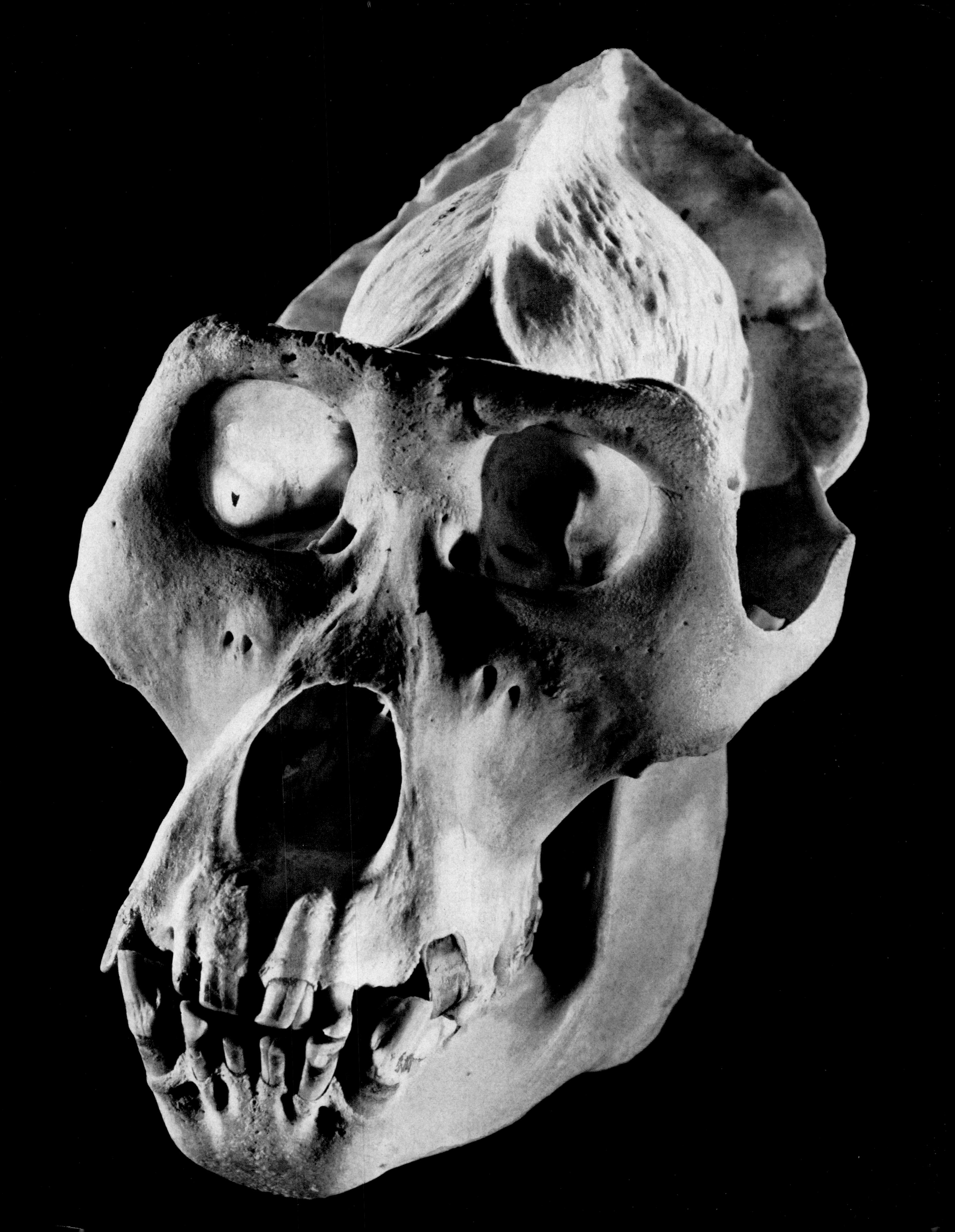

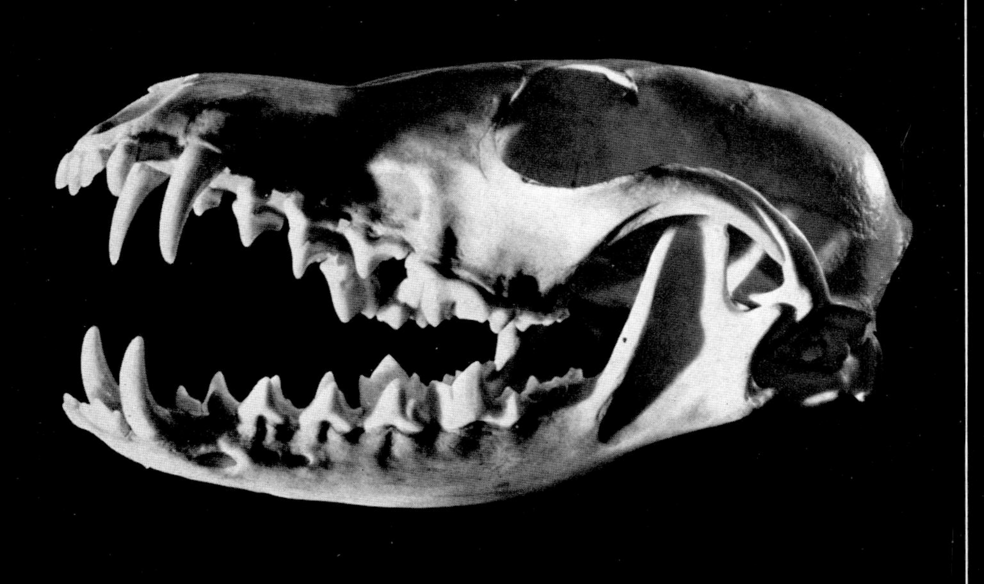
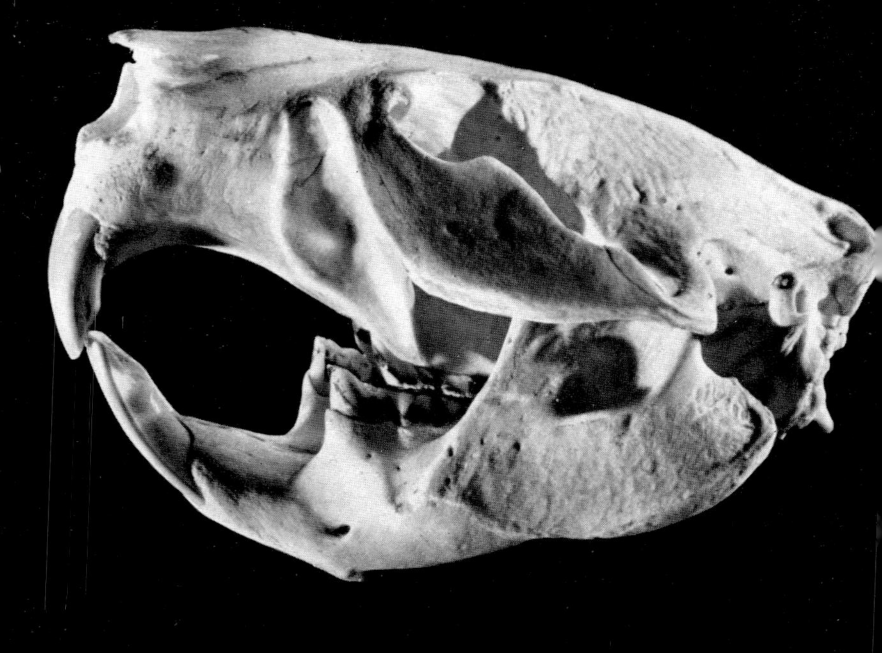
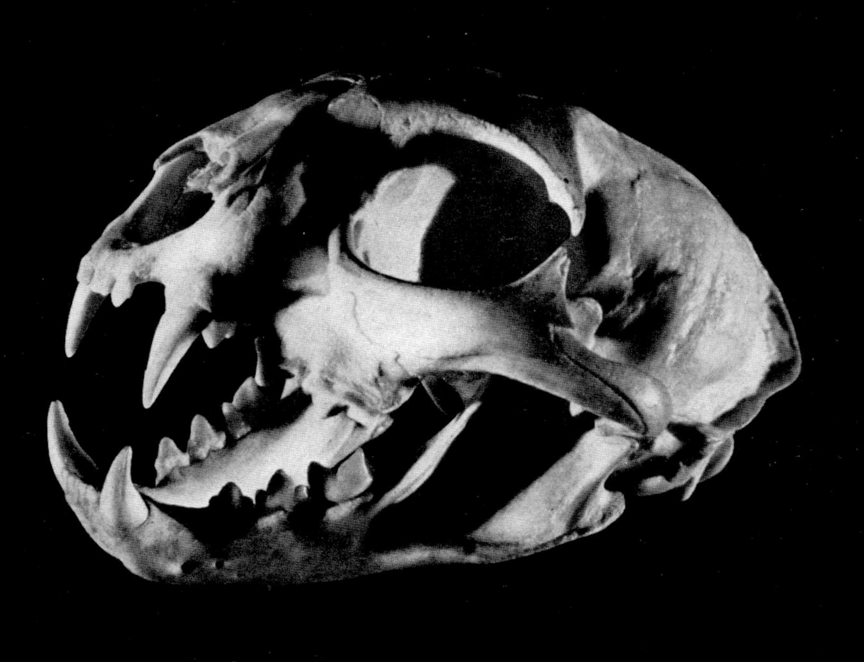
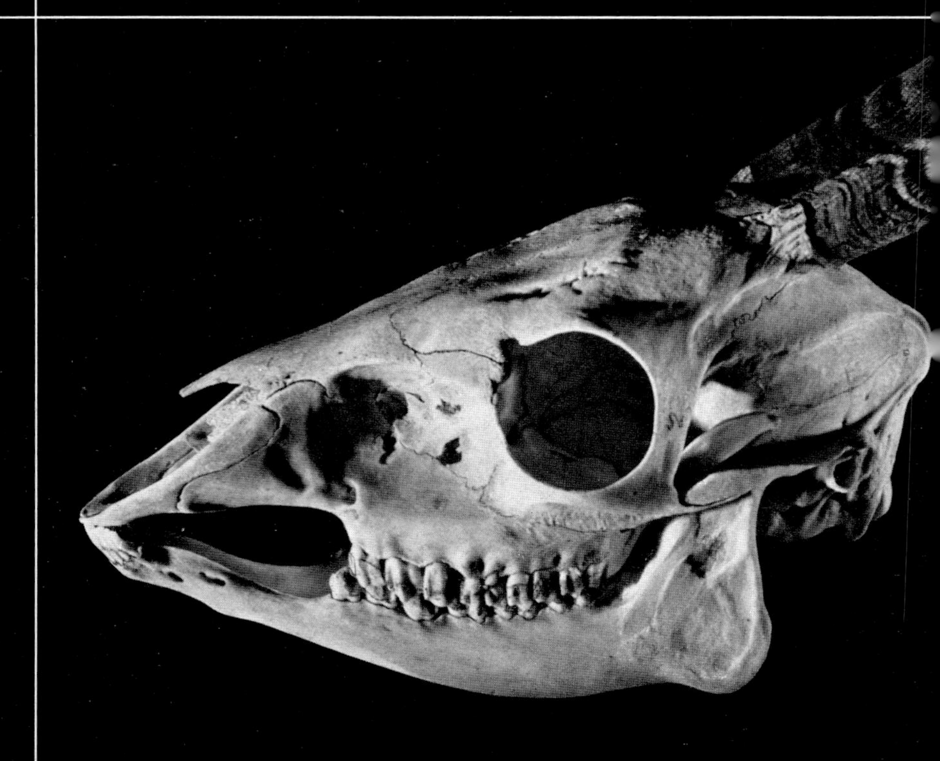
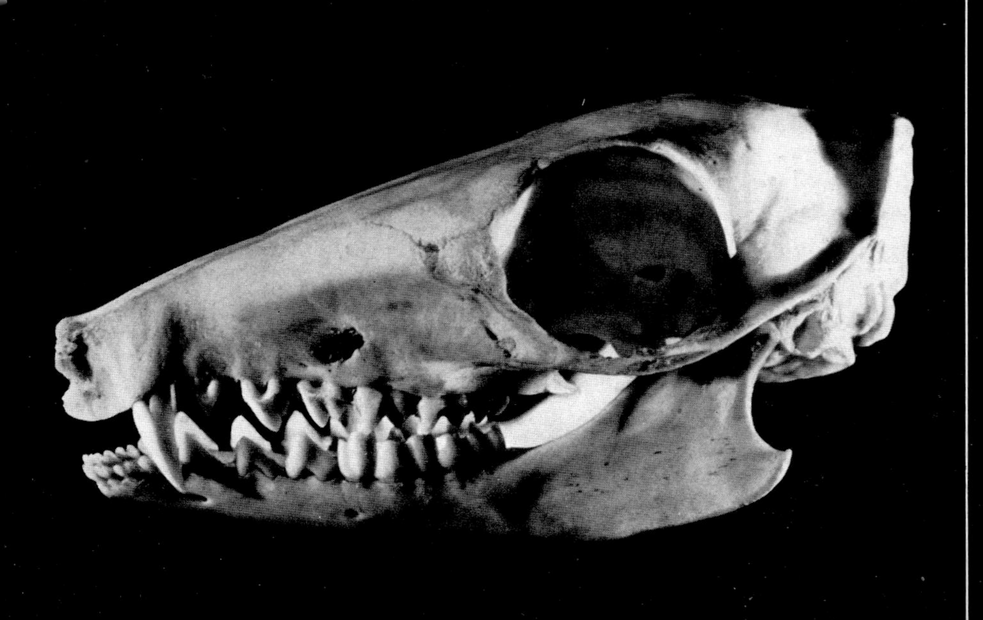
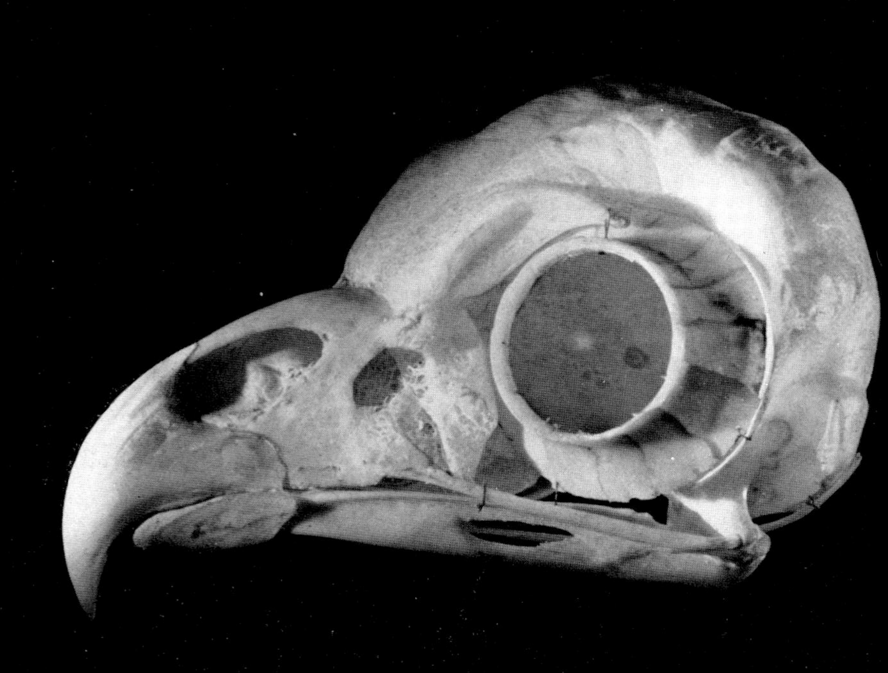

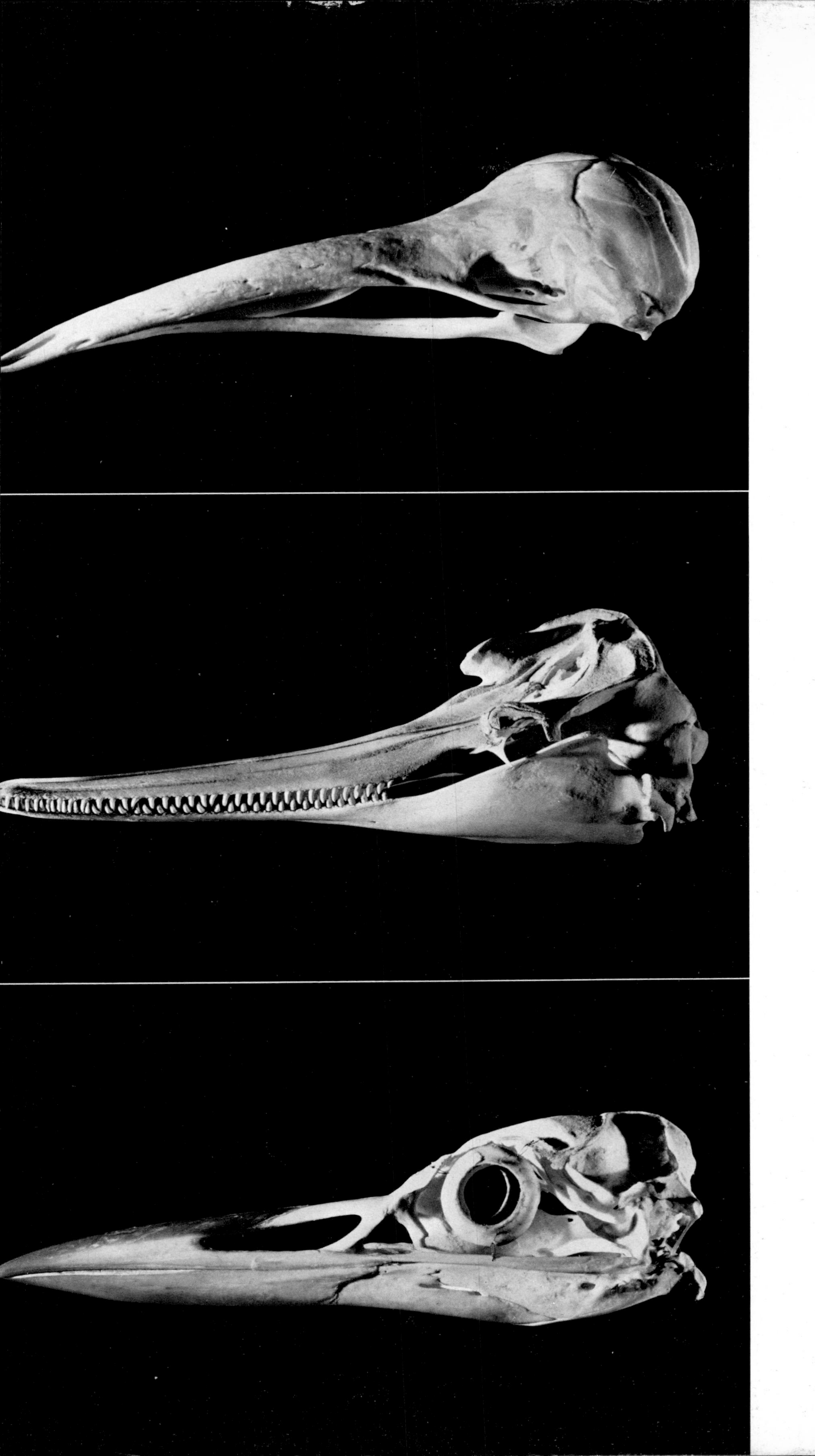

◀132/133 134/135▶

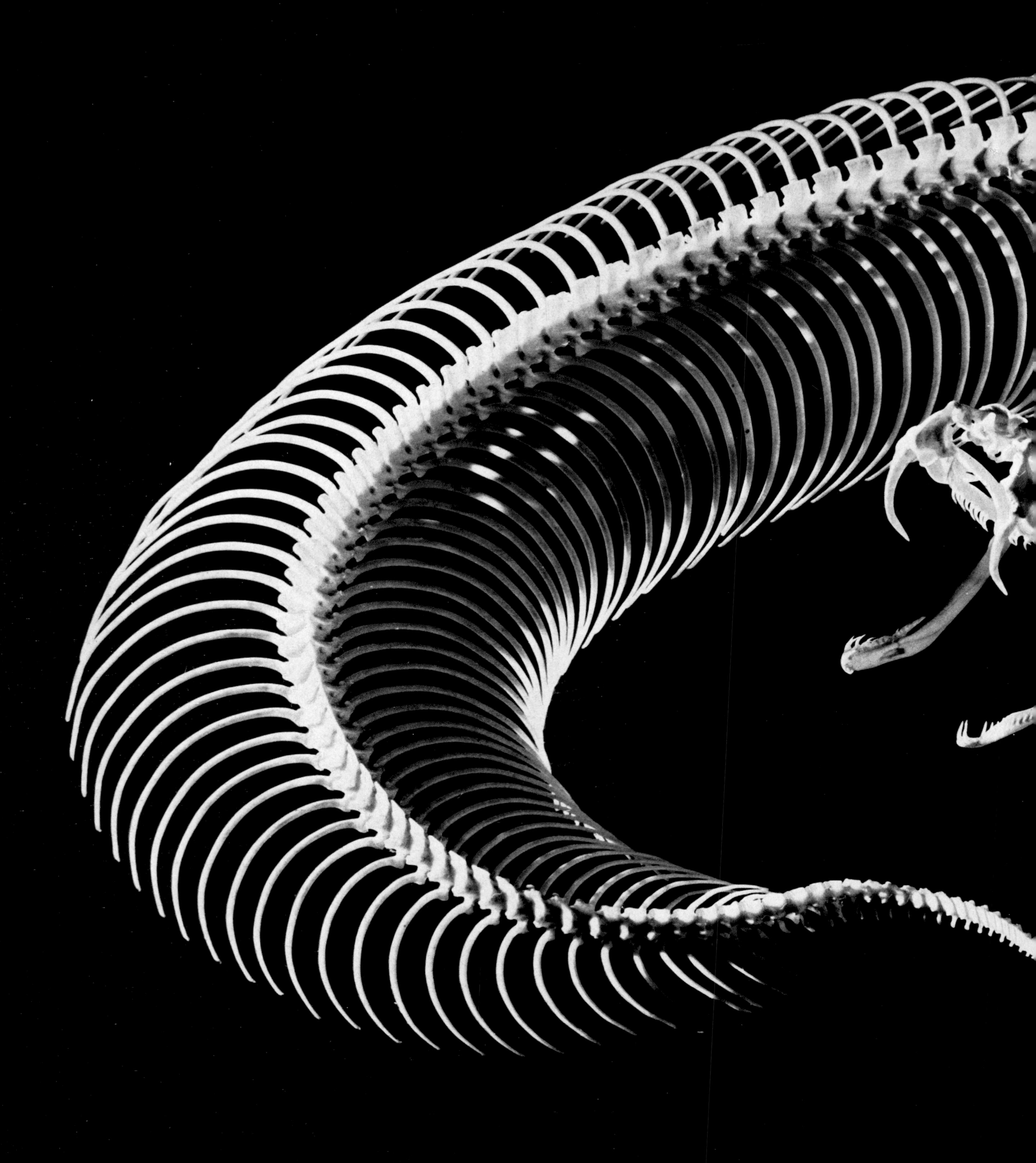

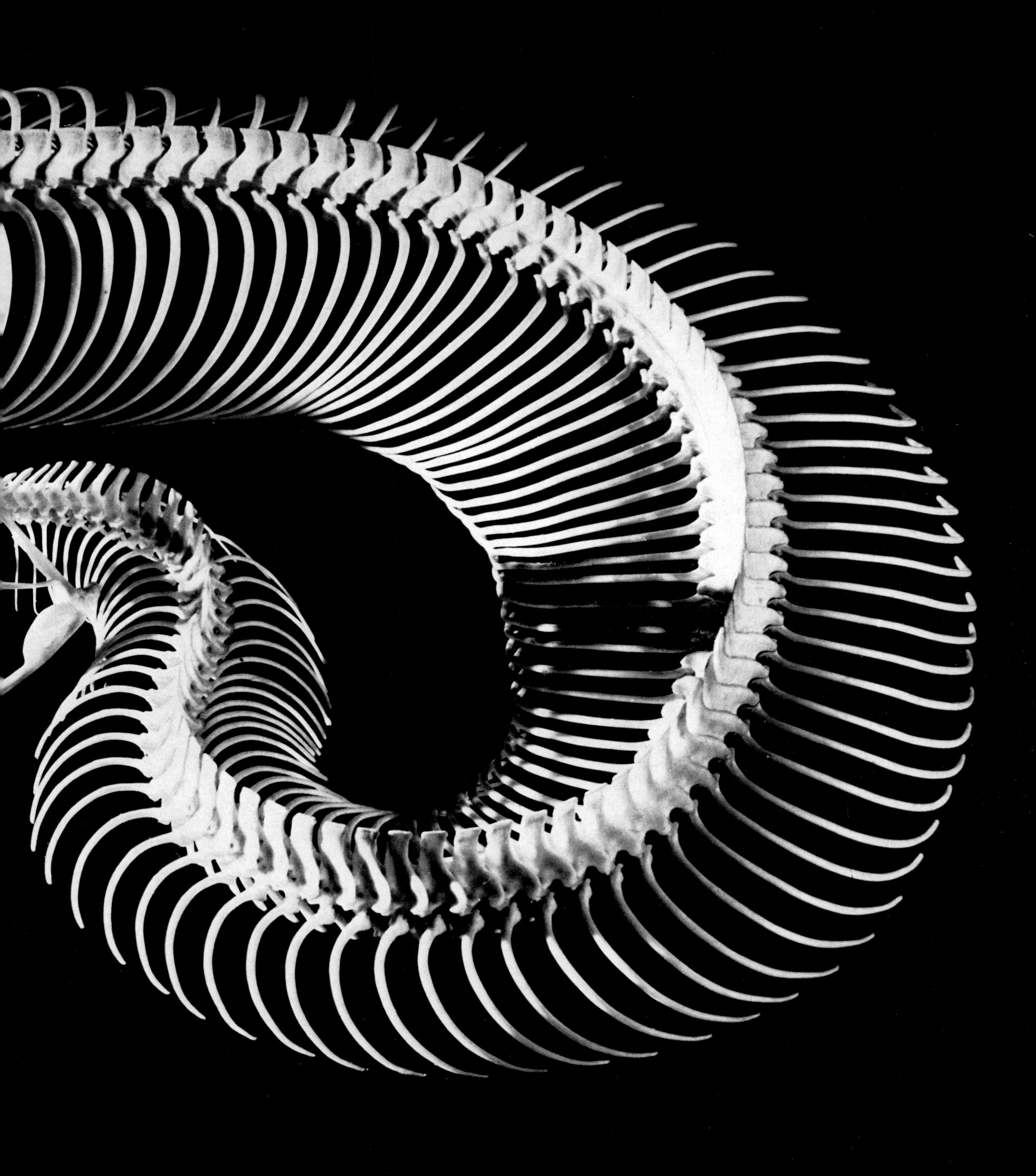

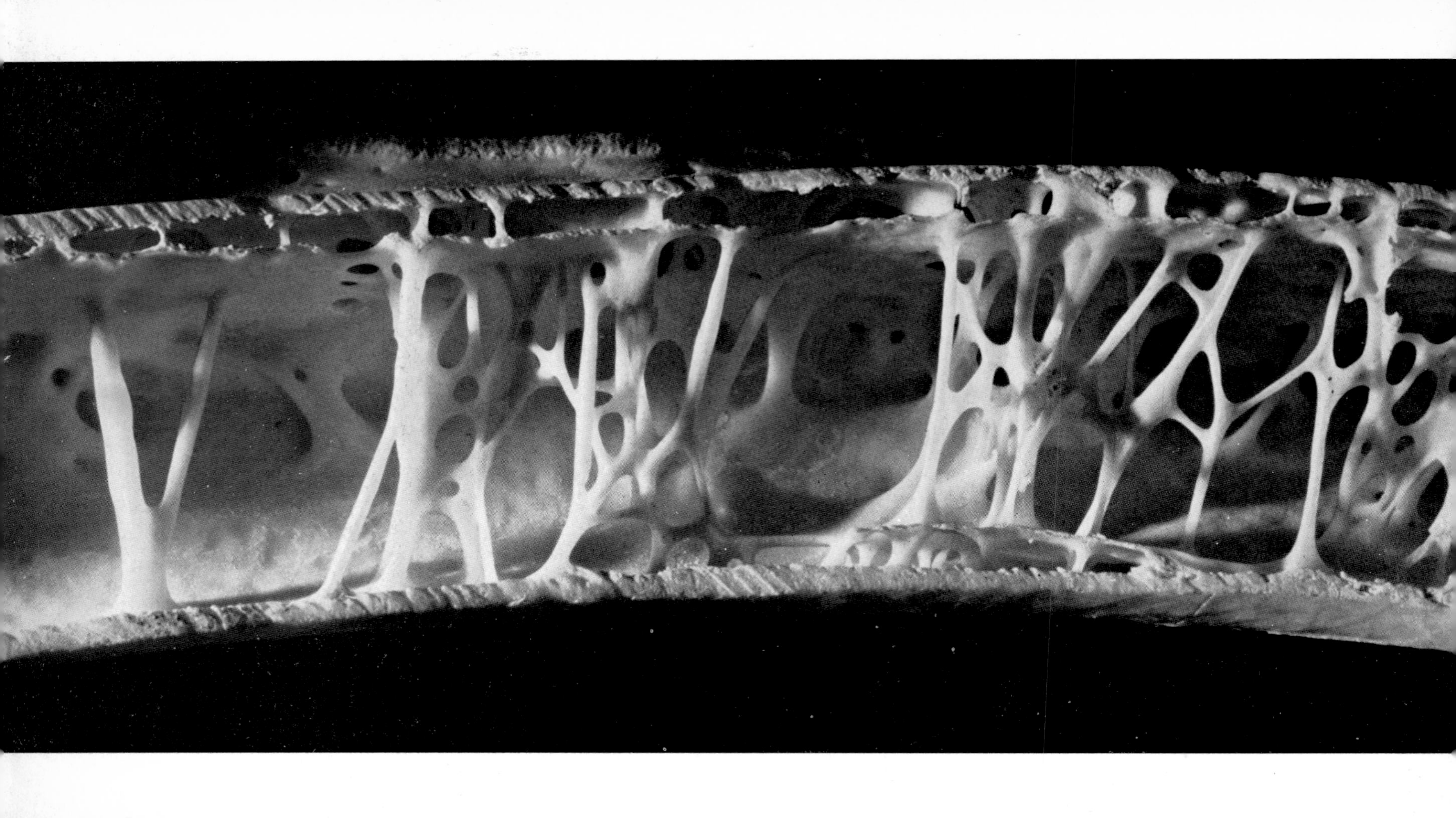

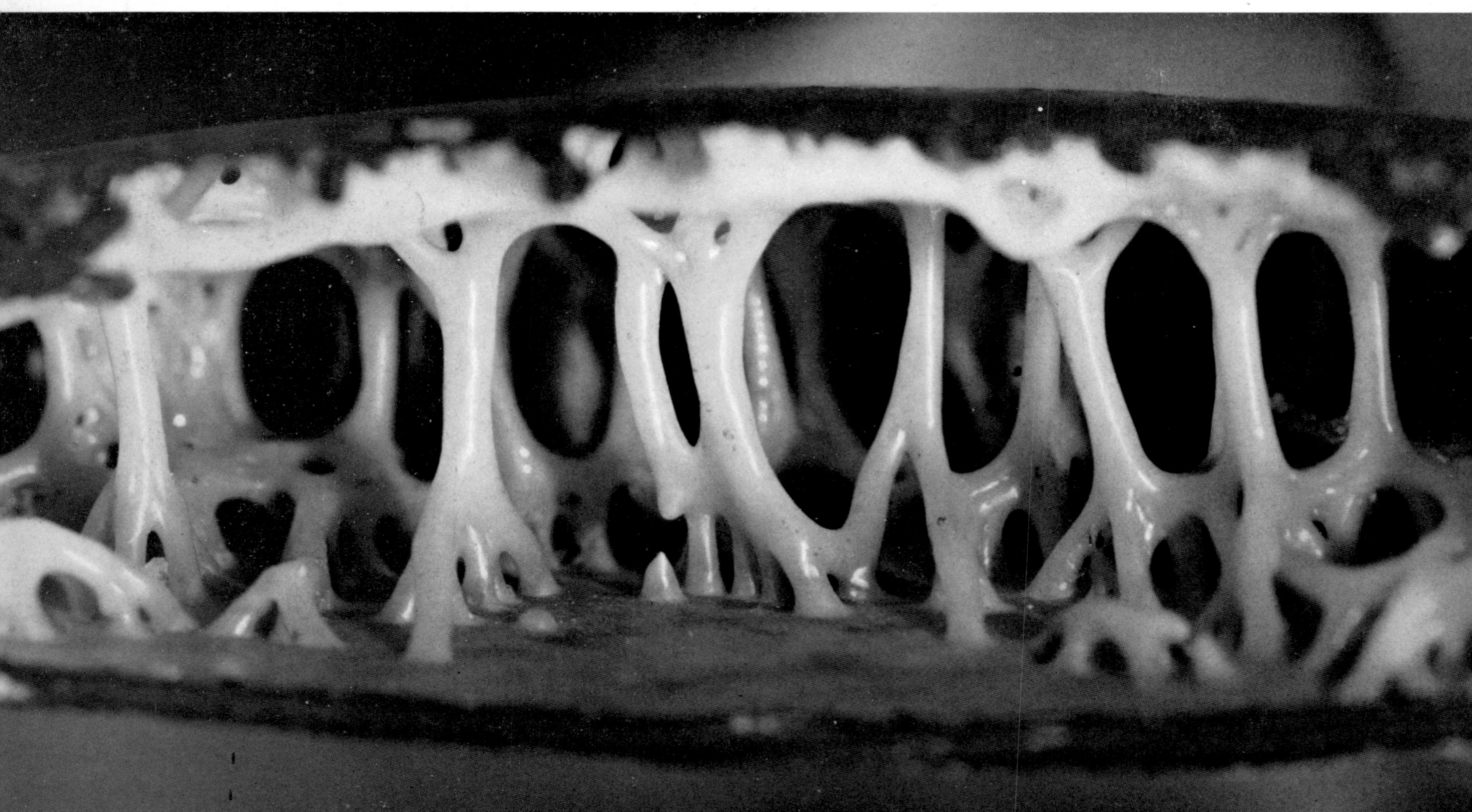

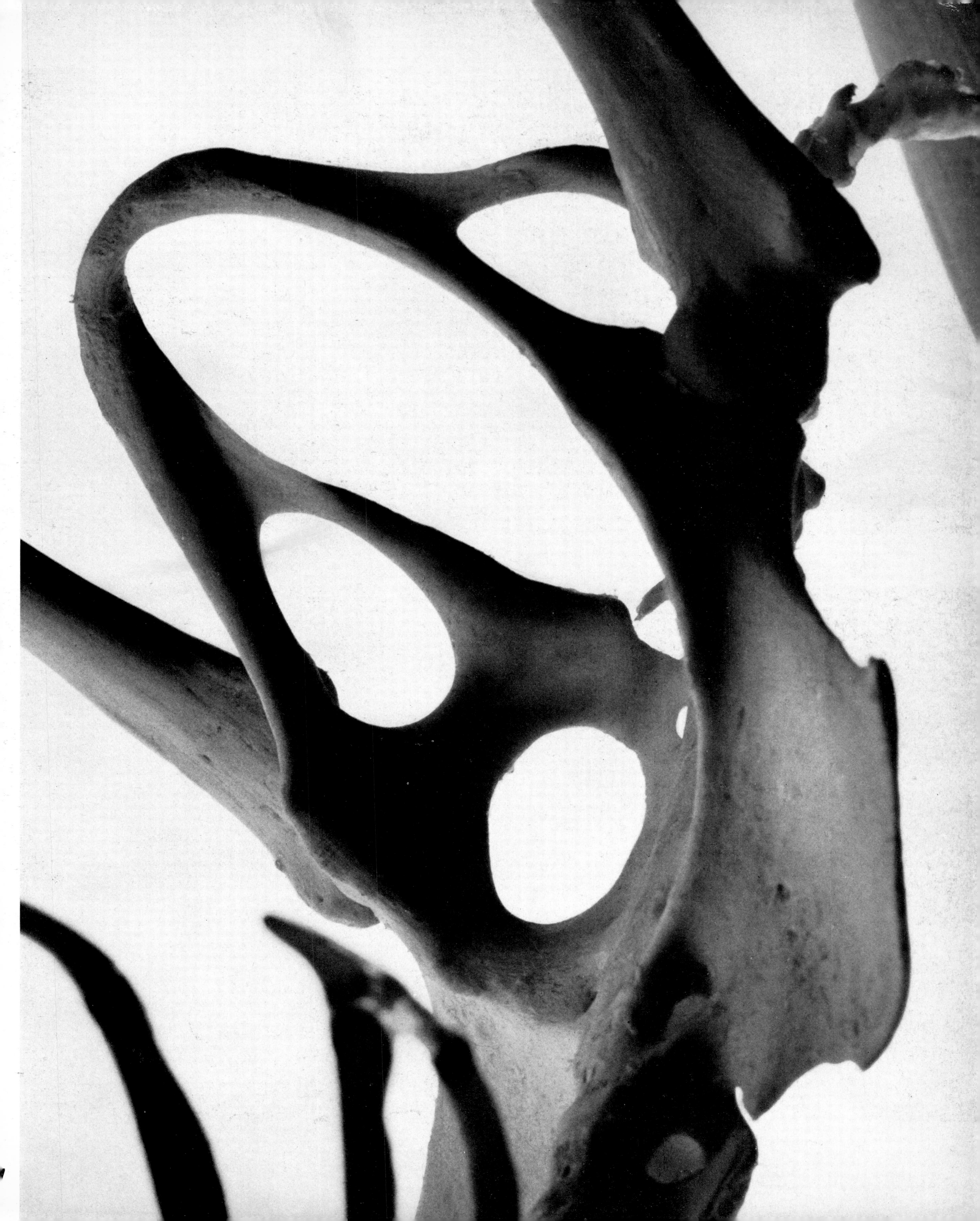

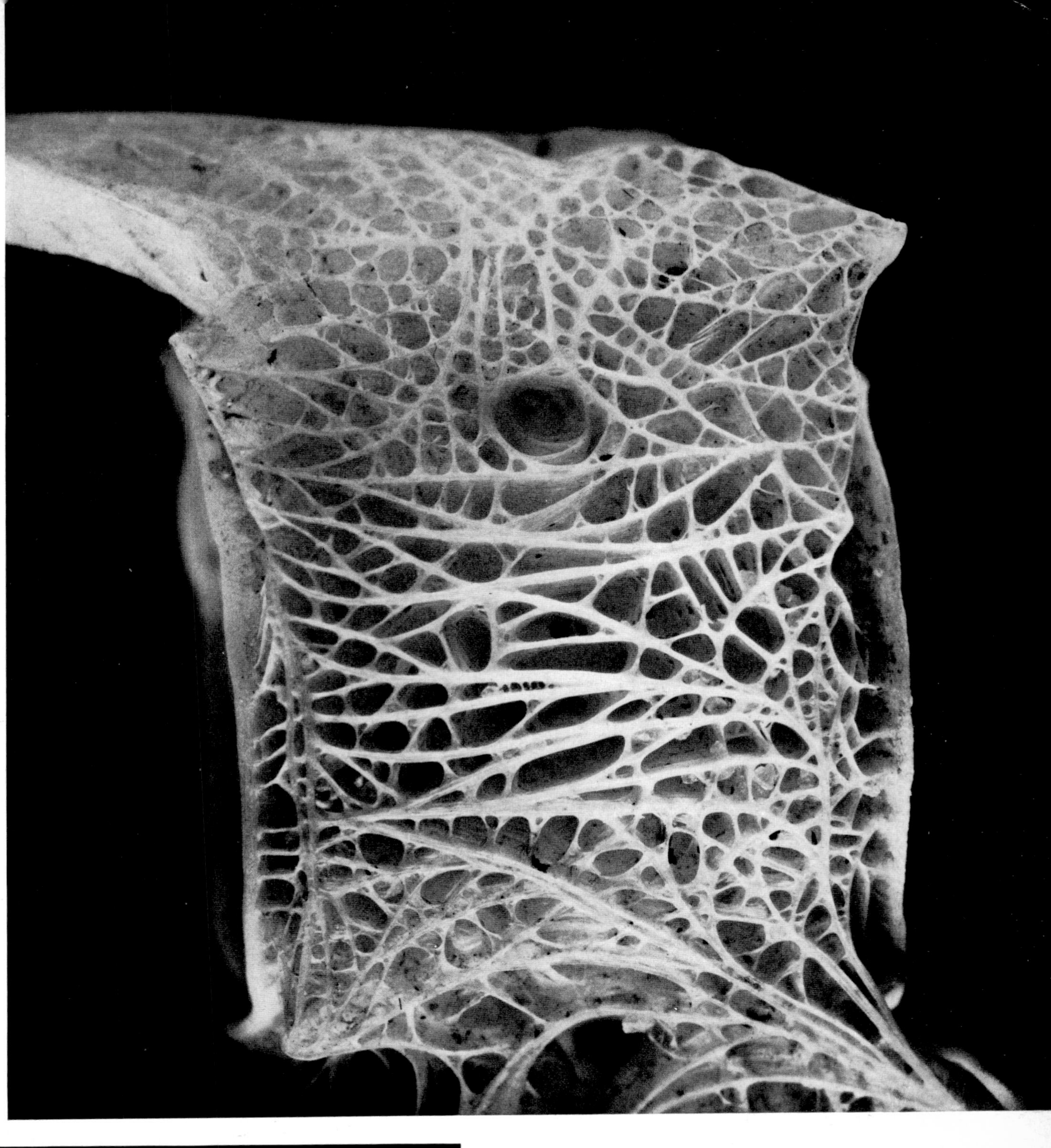

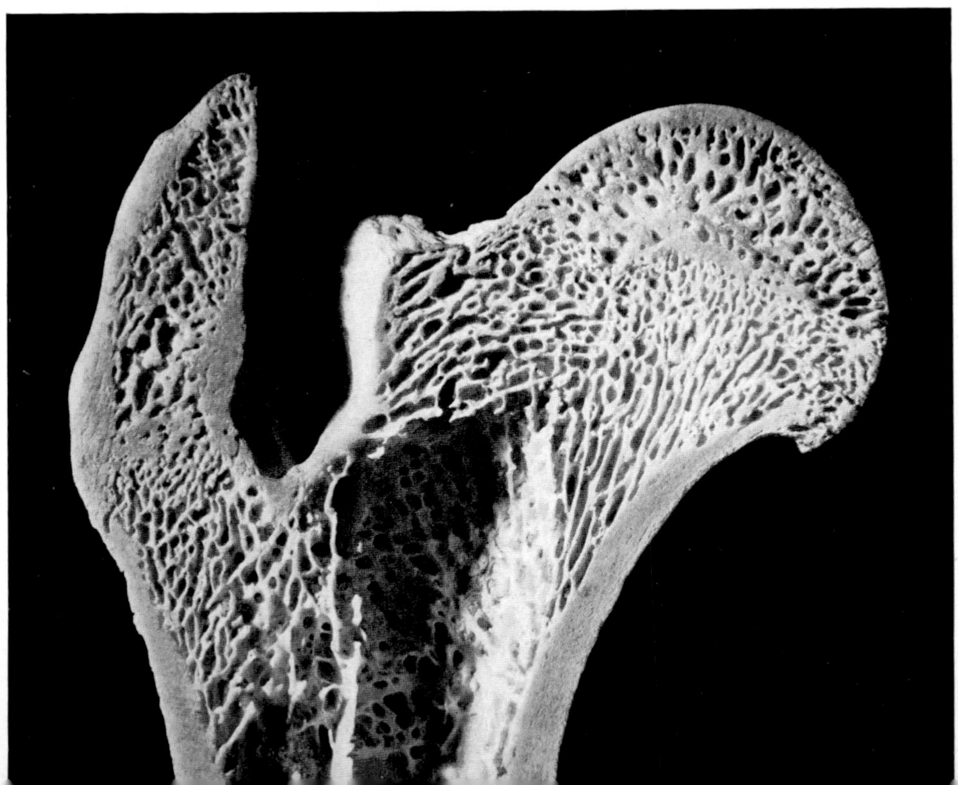

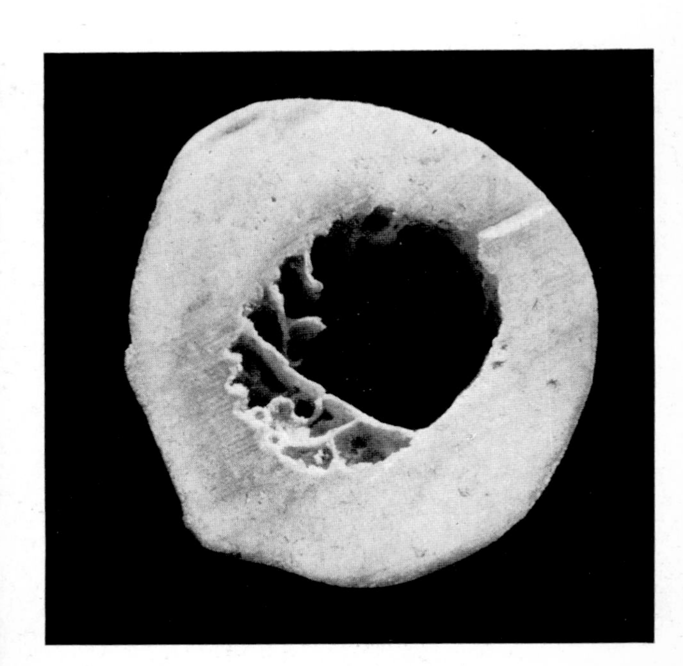

38

39 ▶

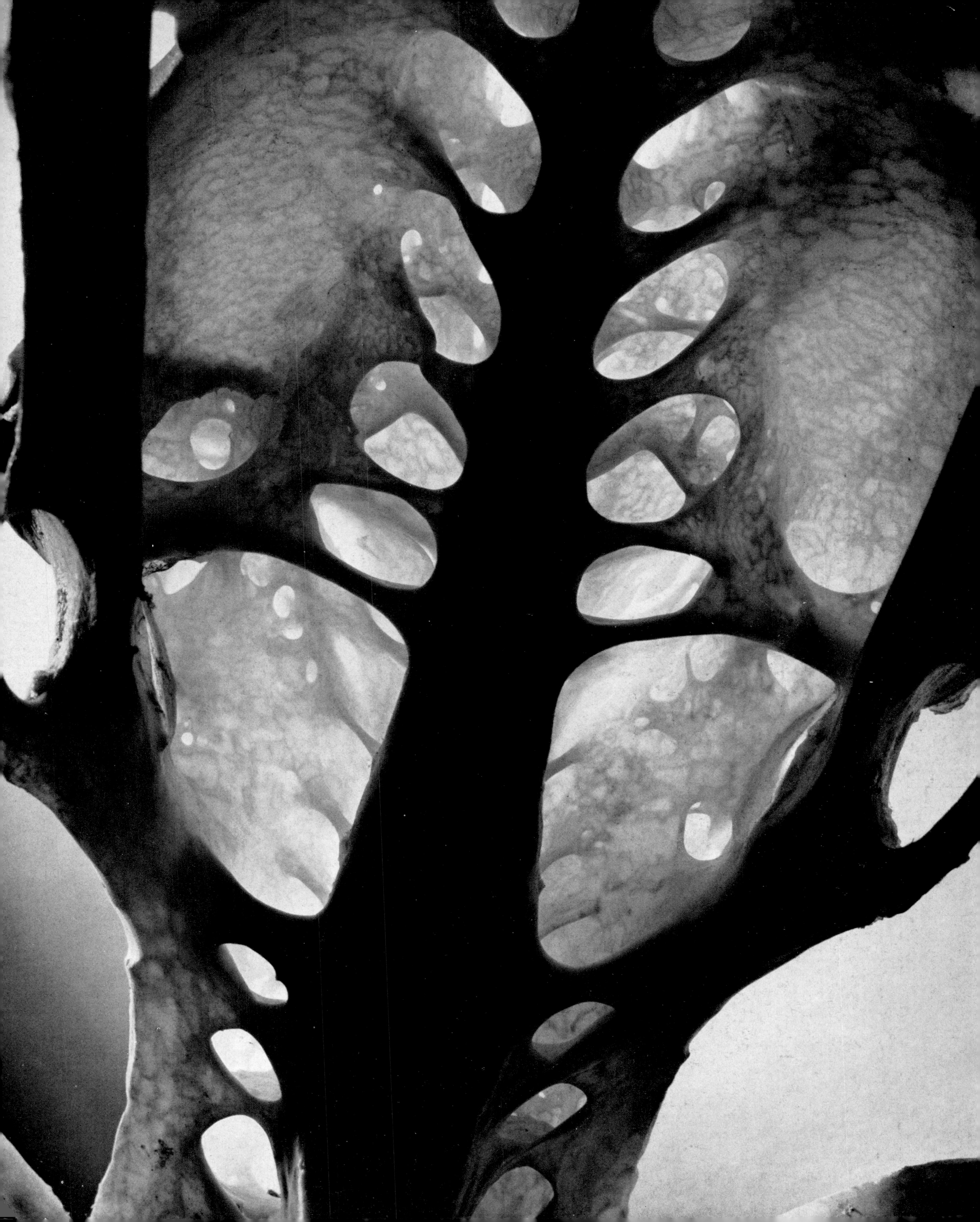

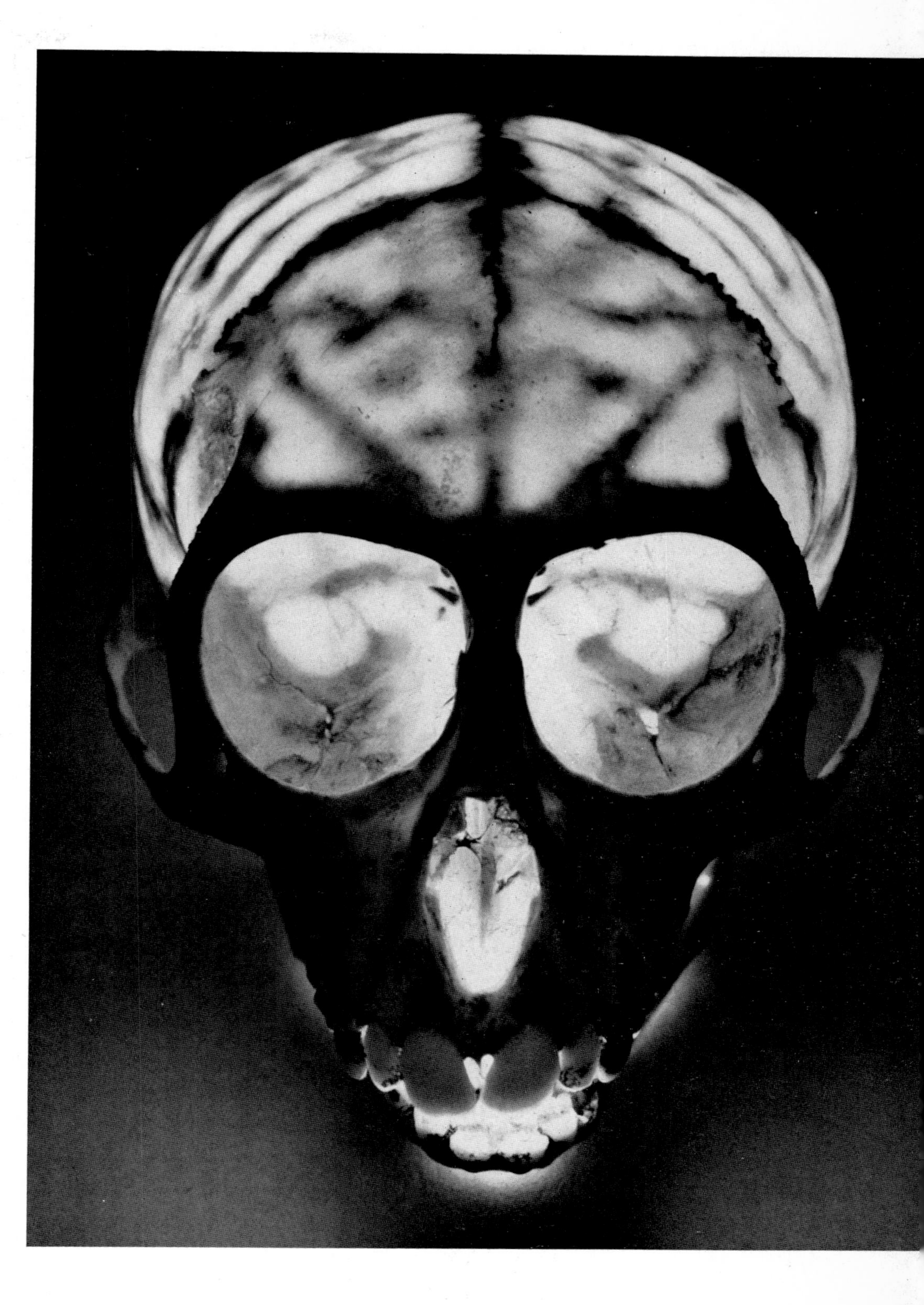

◀ 142
143 ▶

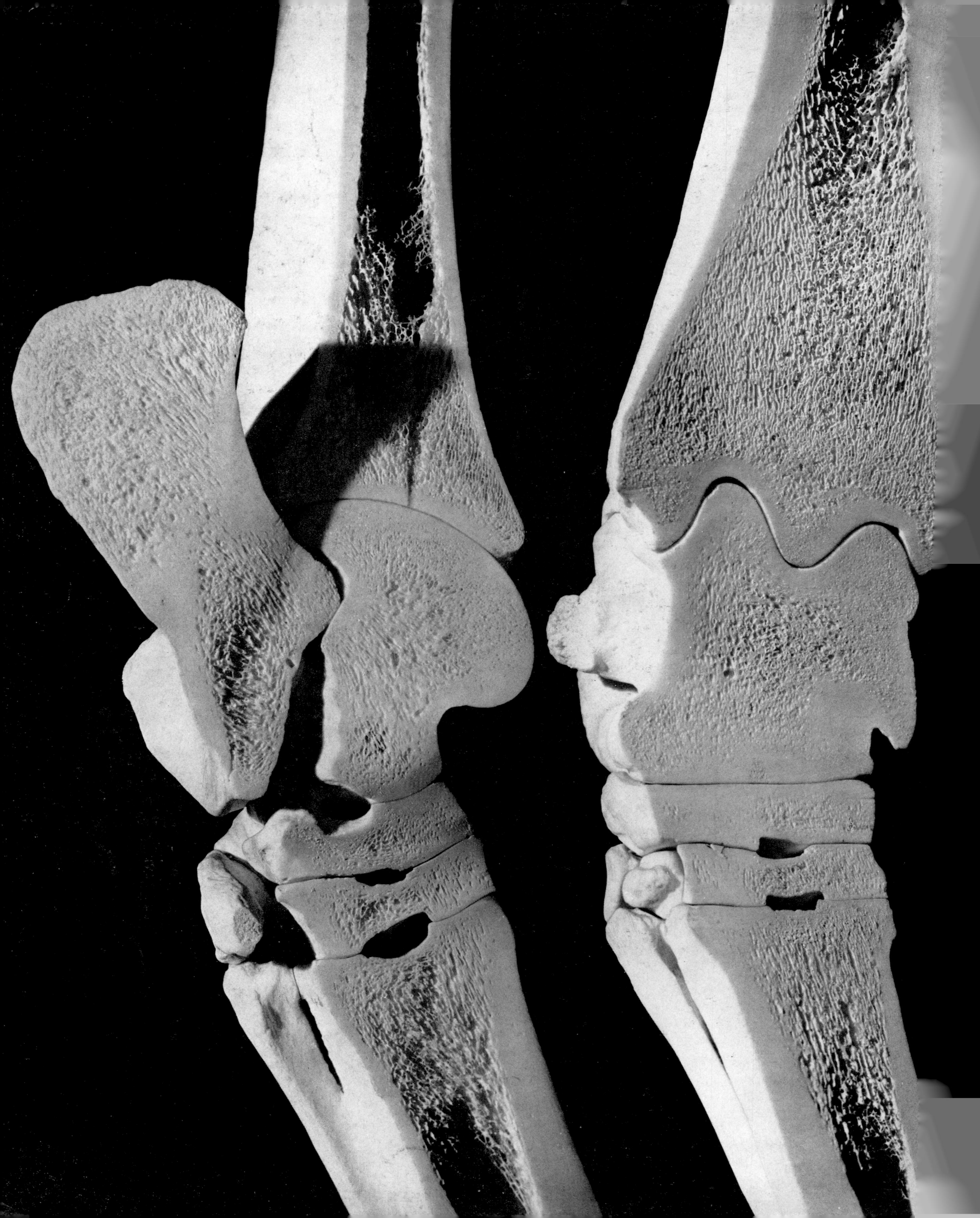

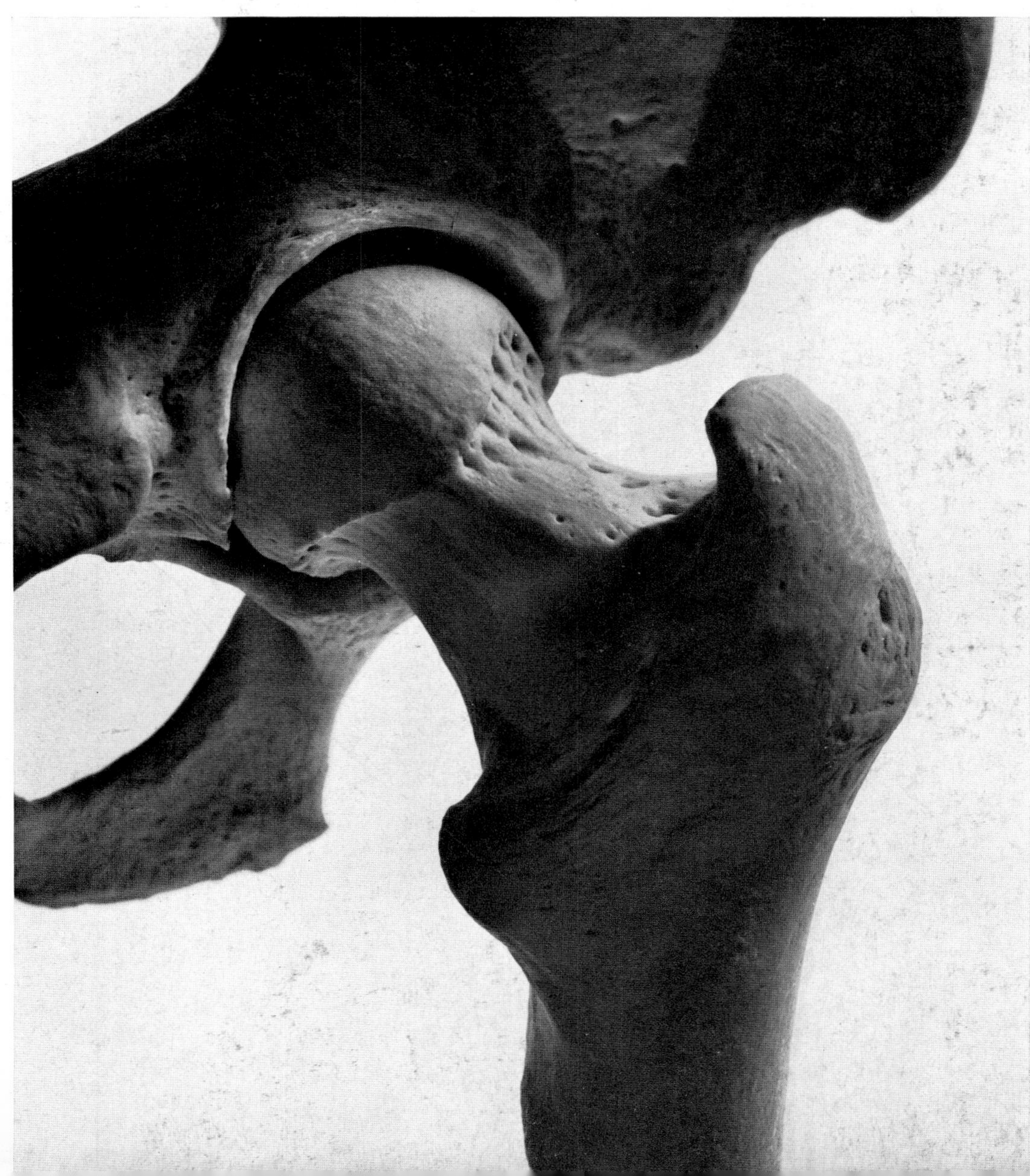

◀144
145▶

XIV

Teeth for Many Purposes

The teeth of mammals can be divided into three groups with different functions. First, there are the front teeth—the incisors—which normally are used for gnawing, cropping, and nipping (a notable exception are the tusks of the elephant, which are highly modified incisors adapted to rooting in the ground, breaking down small trees, and fighting both in attack and defense). Then there are the pointed teeth next to the incisors—the canines—which are primarily used for seizing, killing, and ripping (except for the canines of the ruminants, which look like incisors and fulfill the same functions). And finally, there are the cheek teeth—the premolars and the molars which lie behind them—which are used for shearing, for crushing, or for grinding.

Each of these teeth, however, may be modified to a greater or lesser degree in accordance with the diet of the particular species of animal, which may belong to one of three groups: the flesh-eating animals or carnivores; the plant-eating animals or vegetarians; and the animals which feed on both animal and vegetable matter, the omnivores. Understandably, these food habits are reflected in the shape of an animal's teeth. They are, of course, adapted to deal most effectively with the particular animal's preferred food, which may be tackled in one of three ways: by tearing, grinding, or gnawing.

Animals that tear their food and wolf it down in chunks without chewing it are the carnivores, whose prominent canine teeth and scissors-like premolars and molars are specially designed for tearing and shearing. Typical animals that grind their food are the grass-eaters or herbivores—buffaloes, cows, sheep, deer, antelope, etc.—whose dentition is dominated by broad, flat-topped premolars and molars equipped with abrasive grinding surfaces that are particularly suited to chewing. And animals that first gnaw their food (with their incisors) and then grind it (with their molars) are the rodents—beavers, squirrels, rats and mice, etc.—who can be recognized by their prominent, chisel-like incisors, which are specially adapted to gnaw through seed cases and nutshells as well as bark and wood.

In addition to their main purpose as tools for dealing with food, teeth also commonly serve as weapons for attack and defense and, though rarely, as tools for grubbing and digging. The following pictures show some of the fantastic forms that animal teeth can take.

146. The upturned canine teeth of a wart hog, which may attain a length of eight to ten inches, assume in effect the function of horns. They are used mostly for fighting among males and in defense against predators and are frighteningly effective against all but the largest carnivores.

147. The downward-pointing canine teeth of a walrus—the tusks—are used to dig up clams and shells from the sea bottom and also as weapons both for fighting among the males during the rutting season and in defense against attacks by polar bears.

148. *Top:* Teeth of a female skate, a fish related to the rays and sharks, magnified approximately fifteen times linear. The teeth of the male are spaced farther apart.

Bottom: Two weathered molars of a cow. The three layers of which teeth consist—enamel, dentine, and cement—can be clearly seen. Differential wear of these materials of unequal hardness produces the rough grinding surface of the tooth.

149. Close-up of the dentition of a lion shows the prominent, dagger-like canines adapted to killing and tearing.

◀ 146

150—151. This formidable apparatus, hinged and tooth-studded like a beartrap, is the skeleton of the jaws of an anglerfish, washed up on the beach near Montauk Point, Long Island, New York. Its needle-sharp, rootless teeth break off easily at their base but, like the heads of the mythical Hydra, are steadily replaced by new ones growing up.

152. The protective "teeth," actually spines, of a Venus comb shell. Defensive mechanisms in the form of hard, pointed structures—canines, quills, spines, and thorns—are adaptive characters evolved by both animals and plants, showing that, despite differences of material and construction, elementary principles of function are essentially alike throughout nature.

153. The "tooth-studded" claw of a crab. Although these "teeth" are only protuberances of the exoskeleton, their function is the same as that of certain types of vertebrate teeth—they are tools for seizing and holding.

147 ▶

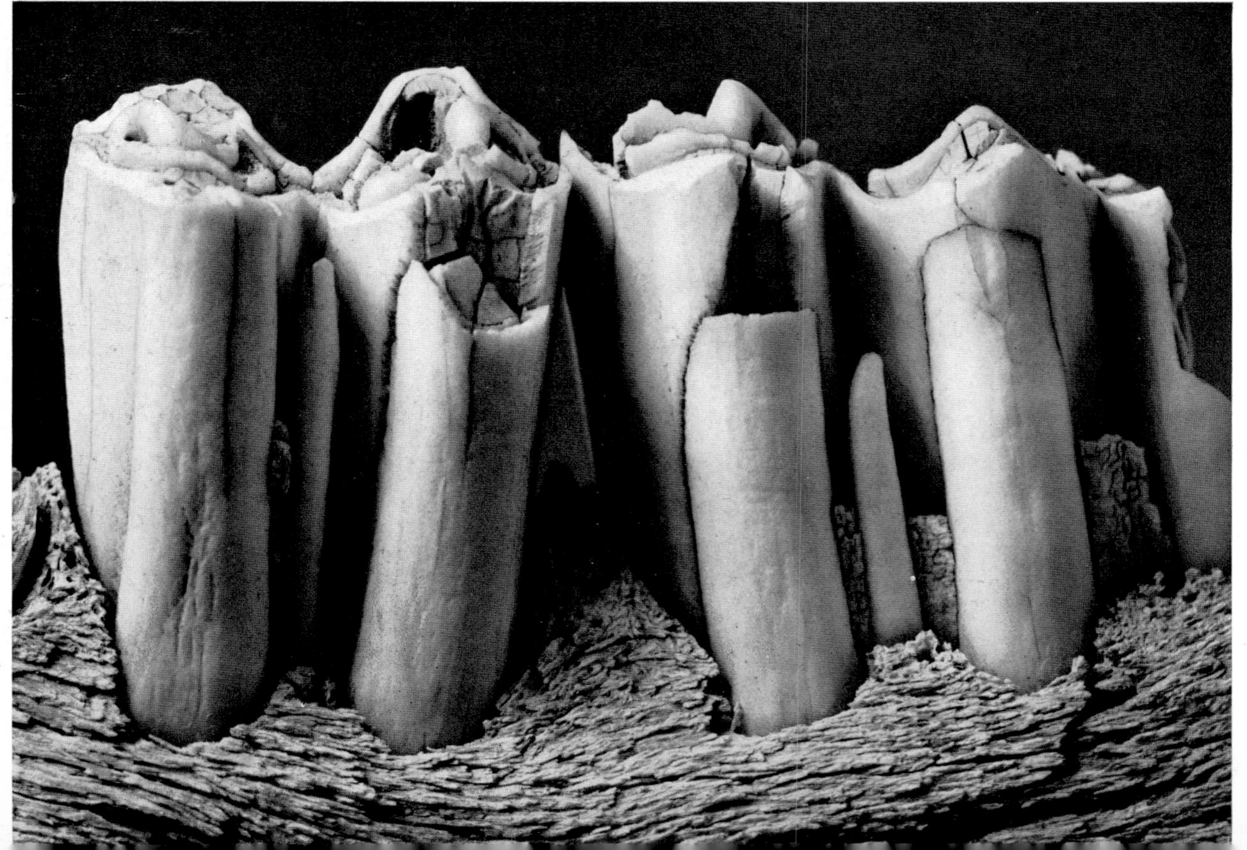

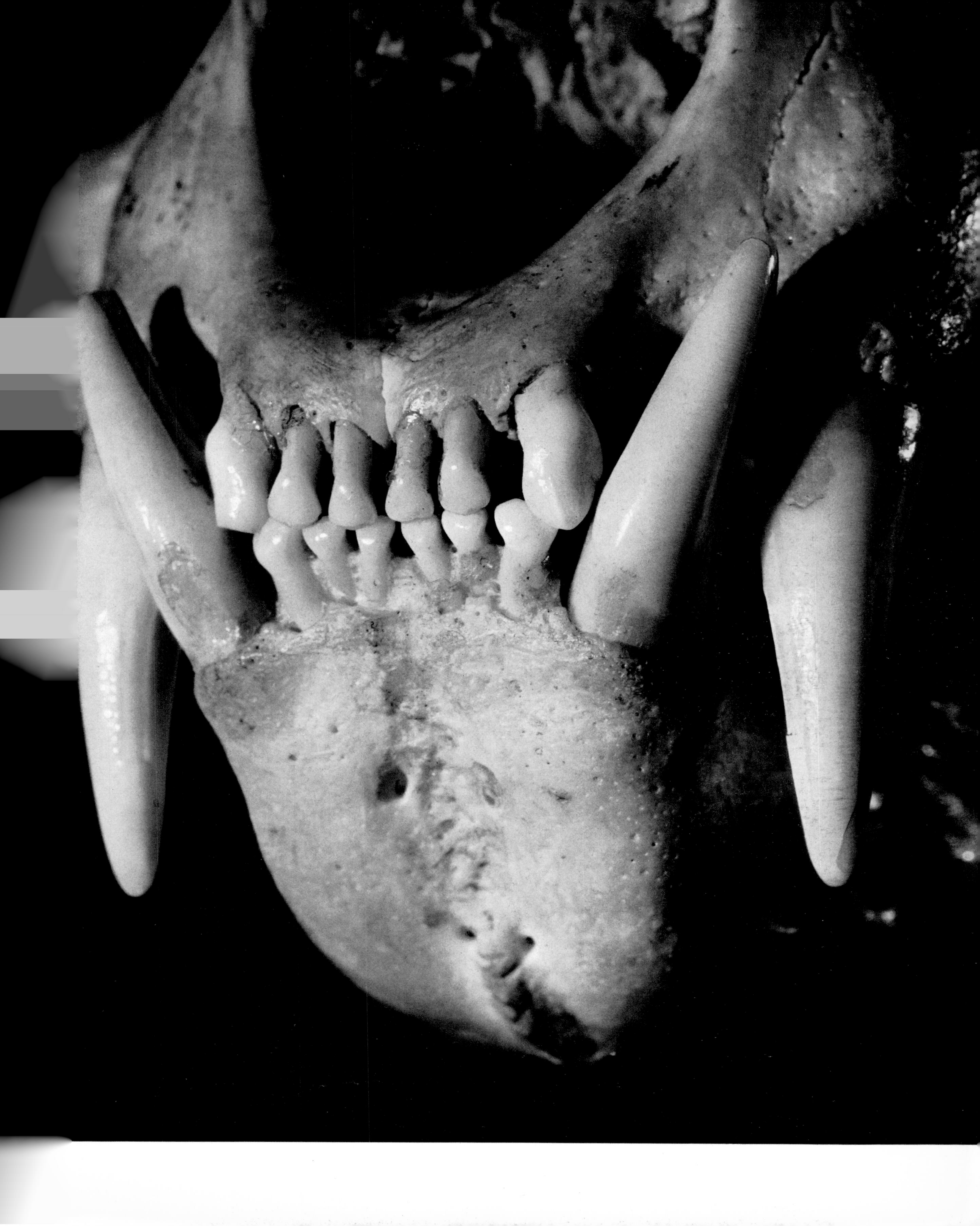

◀152
153▶

XV

The External Skeleton

Of the million or so known species of animals, only some 5 per cent—the vertebrates—have an interior skeleton (endoskeleton). The rest—the invertebrates—are either soft-bodied creatures like the jellyfish, worms, and slugs or, like the radiolarians, corals, starfish, shells, and arthropods, have evolved an encasing outside skeleton (exoskeleton).

The exoskeleton of the arthropods—insects, spiders, centipedes, crabs, etc.—for example, consists of a thickened and hardened skin which owes its strength primarily to an organic compound called sclerotin—a substance somewhat similar to our own hair and nails which in many crustaceans is further strengthened by deposits of calcium salts. It gives form and stability to its owner, provides points of attachment for muscles, and therefore in certain respects takes over the functions of an endoskeleton. However, this is where any similarity of purpose between the two types of skeleton ends.

Compared to an endoskeleton, an exoskeleton has both advantages and disadvantages. Whereas an endoskeleton may be compared to a framework imbedded within the material which it supports, an exoskeleton may be compared to a suit of armor which, like a tin can, completely encloses the living substance of its owner. The first merely provides support. The latter, in addition to giving support, has the advantage of not only providing a certain degree of mechanical protection against enemies but—and this is important to all land animals—also furnishing a nearly impervious shield against desiccation—the ever-present danger that the soft body tissues of these small creatures might dry out. On the other hand, being unyielding (despite extensive articulation furnished by a multitude of joints), an exoskeleton prevents its owner from growing in what to us seems a normal way, that is increasing in size and volume at a more or less uniform rate. Instead, arthropods molt, which means that they shed their exoskeleton from time to time like a discarded glove and grow during the brief period while their newly exposed skins are still soft; then the skin hardens again and forms the new and slightly larger exoskeleton. The disadvantage of molting is that it involves a period during which the animal is completely inactive, helpless, and defenseless. The discarded skin represents valuable material which is lost, but many arthropods thriftily recover it by eating their cast molds.

Like the arthropods, many mollusks—oysters, clams, scallops, snails, etc.—also have an exoskeleton—the shell—which, however, does not consist of sclerotin but is composed primarily of a hard, calcareous substance secreted by these animals. Like the exoskeleton of arthropods, the shell provides its owner with protective armor and, in the land snails, offers a safe retreat into which these mollusks can retire and survive in times of dryness. Unlike the exoskeletons of arthropods, however, the shells of mollusks grow at a more or less uniform rate and hence require no molting.

The following photographs show, strongly magnified, some of the exquisitely beautiful forms which exoskeletons can assume.

154. Head of a dead ground beetle (family Carabidae). Resembling a knight in shiny armor, this predator, which feeds primarily on caterpillars, foreshadows in the details of its exoskeleton tank turrets and ball-and-socket joints. Its powerful mandibles make it a menace to anything weaker than itself.

155. A common millipede (class Diplopoda) coiled in defensive position. Unlike centipedes, millipedes have no venom and are completely harmless. They are mostly scavengers that feed on decaying plant material.

◀154

156—157. Apical views of two snails—a harp snail (*Harpa*) and a sundial snail (*Architectonica*)—shown here in approximately twelve times natural size, reveal the sculptural beauty of their spiral forms.

158—159. Sectionalization of two marine snails—a turret shell (genus Turrilites) and a chank shell (*Turbinella pyrum*)—shows their shells' interior. To increase the structural strength of its protective "skeleton," the chank shell possesses a particularly pronounced inner helix (columella) which also increases the contact surface between the mollusk's body and its shell.

160—161. These two extremes in shell form—the exquisitely delicate, thin-walled, translucent fig snail (genus Pyrula) at the left, and the exuberantly ornate, robust rose-branch murex (*Murex erinaceus*) at the right—give an idea of the infinite variety of designs shells can take.

155-157 ▶

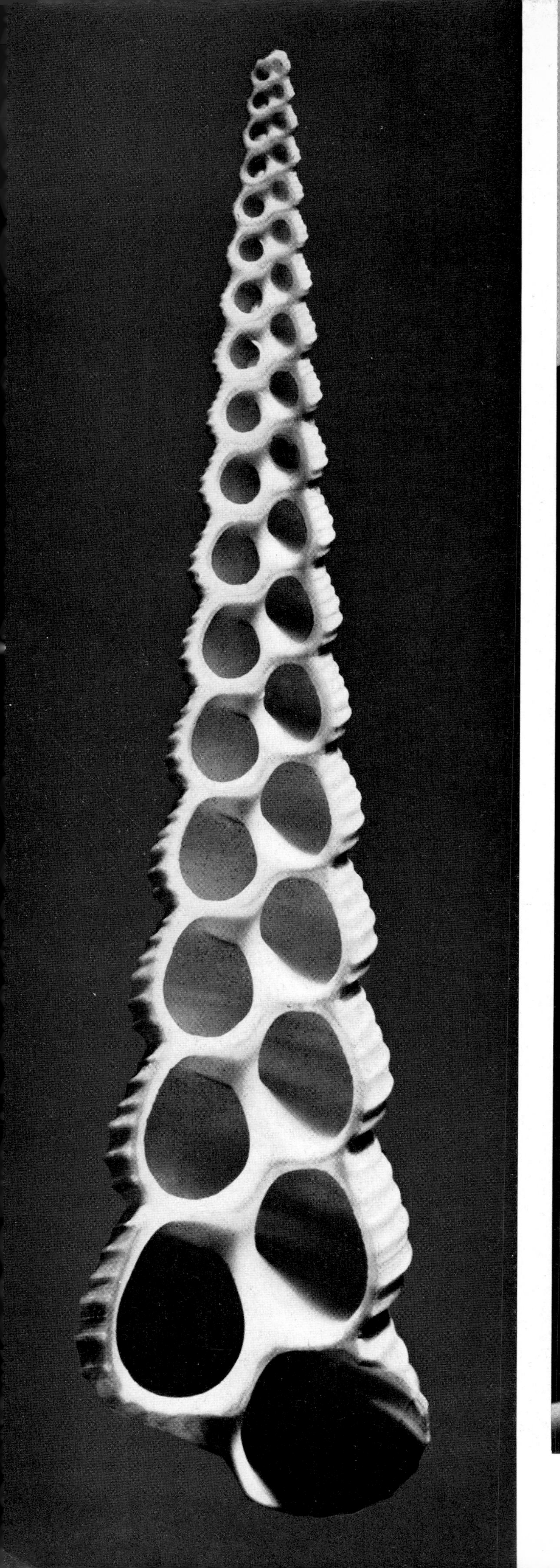

XVI

Radial Symmetry

Except for certain protozoa and most sponges, which are asymmetrical, all animals are designed according to one of three basic body plans: spherical, radial, or bilateral.

Unless affected by other influences, as a result of surface tension, any isolated droplet of liquid will assume a spherical shape. For the same reason, many unicellular animals, being nothing but tiny bubbles filled with viscous protoplasm, are spherical (at least, when at rest) unless stiffened by some kind of skeleton which enables them to maintain some other form. Spherical animals have neither front nor rear, top nor bottom, right side nor left, and can be divided into two identical halves by *any cut in any direction that passes through the center.* A spherical shape is unsuited to directed locomotion but is advantageous to unicellular animals, which are always minute in size and often live in water, where, frequently lacking effective means for moving under their own power, they freely float and drift with current and tide. Typical representatives of spherical animals are the beautiful radiolarias, most of which possess a jewel-like skeleton consisting of the most delicate and exquisite lacework of pure quartz, sometimes in the form of concentric latticed spheres suspended one inside the other like the carved Chinese ivory balls.

Radial-symmetrical animals are built according to a star design based upon a center from which radii go out in all directions. Since these animals are alike all round their periphery, they can be cut into two symmetrical halves by *any lengthwise cut that passes through the center* (but *not* by a crosswise cut because their upper and lower halves are not symmetrical). This lack of spatial orientation is, of course, not exactly conducive to rapid locomotion, and radial-symmetrical animals, all of which live in water, either lead a sessile life or lazily drift around with the currents. Typical representatives of radial-symmetrical animals are the jellyfishes, sea anemones, sea urchins, and sea stars, popularly known as starfish.

And finally, there are the bilaterally constructed animals, all of which have a definite front and rear, and an upper side that is different from the lower side. Such animals can be cut into two symmetrical halves *only by a single cut* following a plane which runs along the long axis of the body from head to tail and from back to belly. Of the three basic body designs, only the bilateral plan is suited to rapid locomotion on land as well as in water and air because it is directly oriented and can therefore be "streamlined." Consequently, all the evolutionary most progressive animals—the vertebrates and arthropods—are built according to this plan.

162. Close-up of the calcareous skeleton of a coral whose design, although seemingly bilateral, is in fact based upon radial symmetry.

163. This is the underside of a starfish skeleton (*Asterias vulgaris*), consisting of a network of articulated, joined calcareous plates, some of which have calcareous spines.

164—165. Upper and lower surfaces of the calcareous skeleton of a five-holed sand dollar (order Clypeastrina), which, unlike the articulated skeleton of a sea star, consists of interlocking, immovable plates. When alive, these animals, which, like the sea stars, belong to the phylum Echinodermata, are covered with short, movable spines and slowly move around on hundreds of tiny tube-feet operated by hydrostatic pressure.

166—167. The influence of radial design on plants is evident in these two pictures of a maple leaf and a mushroom. Although actually bilateral, these forms show how nature may combine the best of two different designs when it is in the interest of the respective organisms.

◀ 162

168—169. The calcareous skeletons of stony corals. At the left, a broken piece of coral well rounded by the grinding action of the surf. At the right, a close-up of the individual cups magnified approximately twelve times linear. In life, these limy skeletons are covered with masses of the often very colorful, exquisitely delicate, blossom-like polyps which secreted them and lived in the sheltering security of their craters.

170. This is the personal signature of a mushroom—the fruiting body of a fungus. It was made by direct contact between the cap of the mushroom and a piece of paper. Placed there overnight, the mushroom shed its microscopic spores, which fell straight down and left this imprint of its gills, proving that true radial symmetry is a form of design found in the structures of both animals and plants.

163 ▶

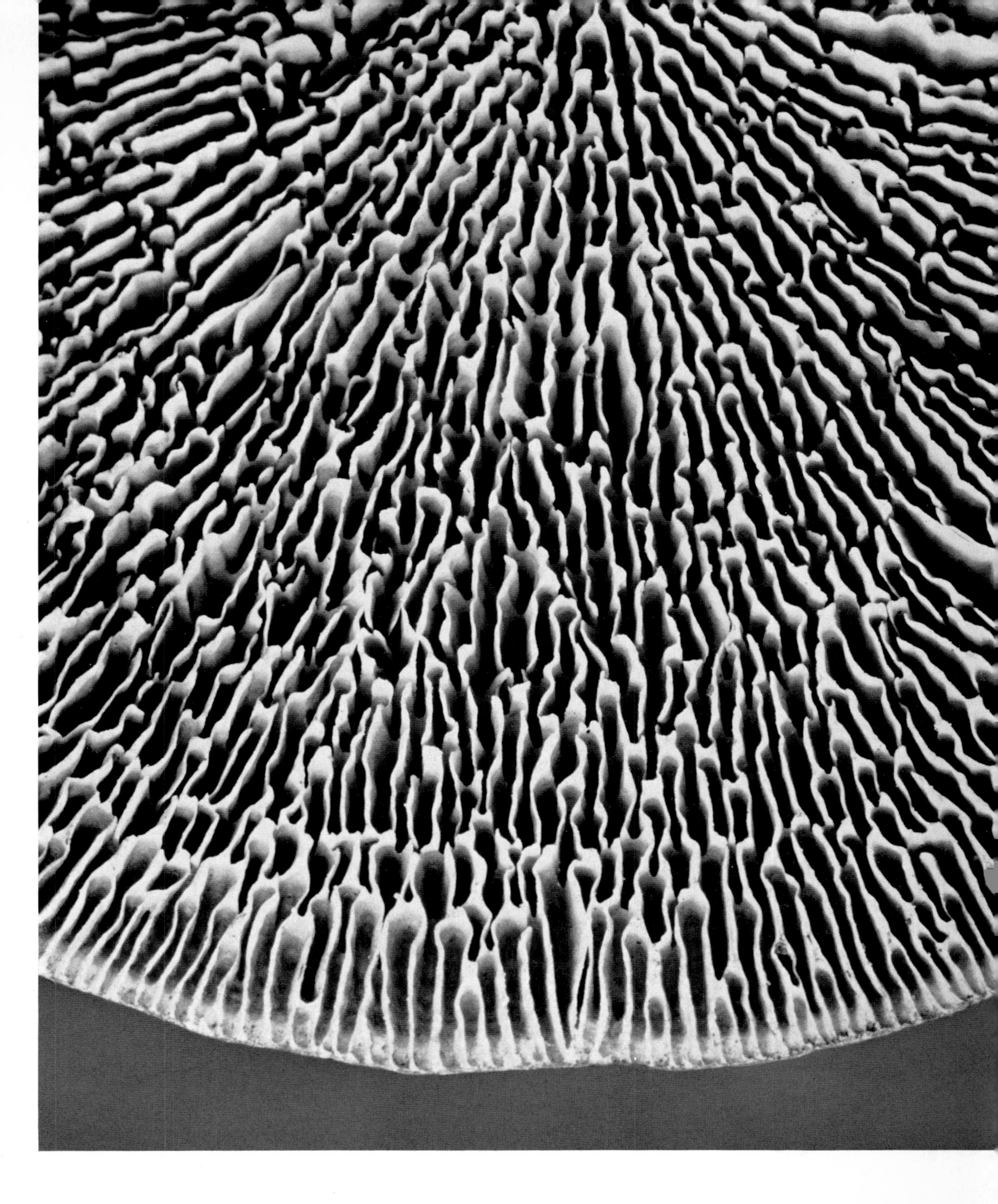

◀ 166
167 ▶

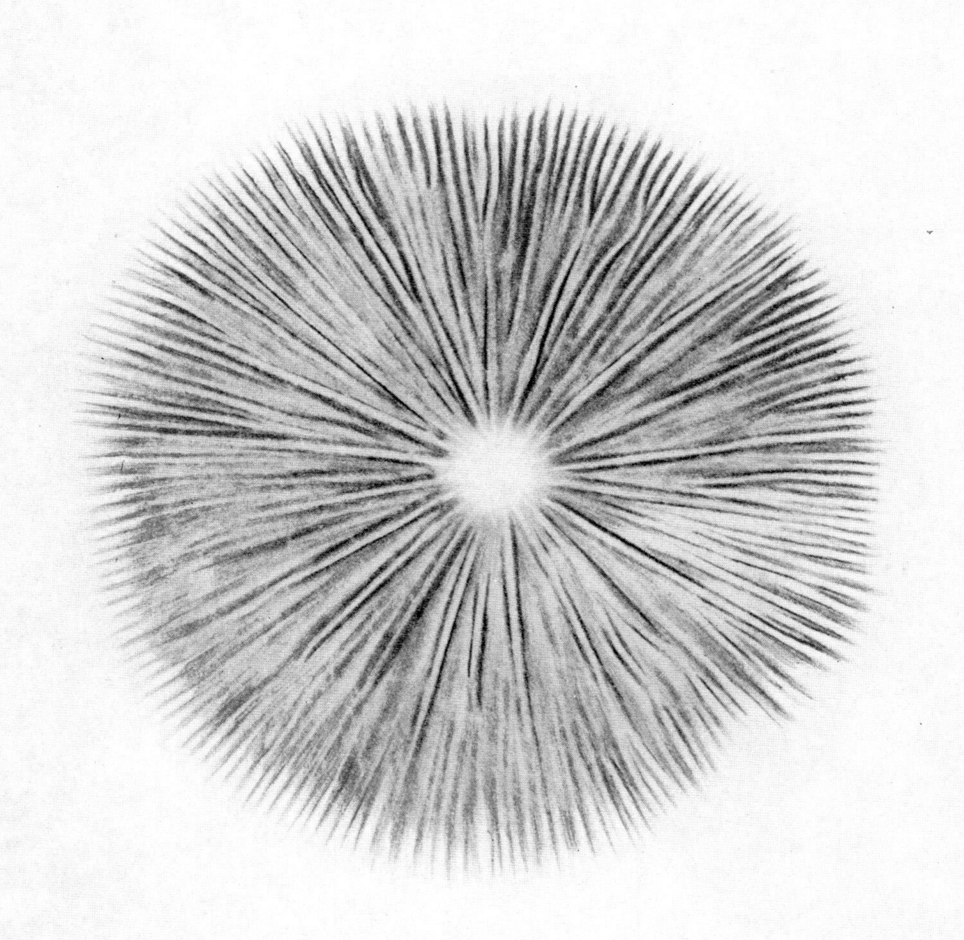